EDITORS' ASSOCIATION OF CANADA

Meeting Editorial Standards

REVISED EDITION

Volume 1
Self-Tests

Toronto, Ontario

For information on reprint permission, see volume 2, page 271.

Co-published and distributed by Captus Press Inc., 14 &15, 1600 Steeles Ave. W., Concord, On L4K 4M2 Canada

Orders

Telephone: (416) 736-5537   E-mail: info@captus.com
Fax: (416) 736-5793   Internet: www.captus.com

Canadian Cataloguing in Publication Data

Main entry under title:

Meeting editorial standards

Rev. ed.
Co-published by Editors' Association of Canada
Contents: v. 1. Self-tests — v. 2. Solutions and discussion
ISBN 1-55322-004-8 (set)   ISBN 1-55322-002-1 (v. 1)   ISBN 1-55322-003-X (v. 2)

1. Editing — Standards — Canada. I. Editors' Association of Canada

PN162.M44 2000   808'.027   C00-931417-2

Care has been taken to acquire reprint permission for copyrighted material contained in these volumes and to acknowledge all such indebtedness accurately. The publisher will gladly accept information that will permit any errors or omissions to be rectified in future printings.

The drawing on the front covers is a digitized version of an illustration printed in 1491 by Johann Schoensperger.

The abstract illustrations throughout these volumes are by Brian Henderson and reprinted, with his permission, from *The Alphamiricon*, Toronto: Underwich Editions, 1987.

The style sheet and three stories of *The Southgate Approach* are adapted from the files of *The Four Winds Sentinel*, a monthly newspaper published in University City, a community in North York, Ontario.

The sample table in A Table for a Friend is from Irene K. Ip, *Big Spenders: A Survey of Provincial Finances in Canada*, Policy Study 15, Toronto: C.D. Howe Institute, 1991, p. 154, table 4.2.

The Bosun's Chair is adapted from Brian Buchanan and Robert Cardarelli, "Bosun's Chair Used for Surface Review of Walls," *The Condominium Manager*, Winter 1993, pp. 28–29.

A Teacher's Manual is adapted with permission of Harcourt Brace & Company, Canada from pp. 108–116 of the *Teacher Resource Book for All over the World* in the *Impressions* series by Jack Booth, David Booth, Jo Phenix, and Larry Swartz, © Holt, Rinehart and Winston of Canada, Limited, 1988.

Portions of the bibliography are adapted from Riça Night, *A Beginning Freelance Editor's Bookshelf*, rev. (Toronto, 2000); and from *Tools of the Trade: An Annotated Bibliography of Reference Sources for Editors and Writers*, compiled by members of EAC Quebec/Atlantic Canada (Montreal: EAC/ACR QAC, 1995).

We thank the holders of copyright for permission to reprint, adapt, and introduce errors for instructional purposes. We are also grateful to the University of Chicago Press, which gave us detailed information on changes in the fourteenth edition of *The Chicago Manual of Style*.

Set in Monotype Dante by Jonathan Paterson

03 04 05   6 5 4 3 2

Contents

Acknowledgments

These two volumes of *Meeting Editorial Standards* were created by members of the Committee on Professional Standards of the Editors' Association of Canada (formerly the Freelance Editors' Association of Canada): Lenore d'Anjou, Dennis Bockus, Catherine Cragg, Riça Night, Shaun Oakey, Jonathan Paterson, Elizabeth Reid, Stephen Roney, Cy Strom, and Jim Taylor. The task was exciting but often challenging for volunteers whose schedules are set by the exigencies of full-time editing as well as their personal lives.

Several other people helped by writing or contributing to pieces. They were Lydia Burton, Madeline Koch, Dennis Mills, Wendy Thomas, and Penny Williams.

An early version of the tests was sent to a group of experienced editors who work in a variety of genres. Their review culminated in a weekend-long session of comments and discussion. Participants were Jane Buckley, Barbara Czarnecki, Heather Ebbs, Bernard Kelly, Dennis Mills, Maureen Nicholson, Eleanor Sinclair, Wendy Thomas, and Jean Wilson. Olga Domján, Anthony Luengo, and Penny Williams also gave valuable insights.

After much revision, the document was sent out, section by section, to a team of second reviewers. Working in isolation and with tight deadlines, they may have faced an even harder task. Each test and answer key was read by three of the following: John Eerkes, Freya Godard, Prue Hemelrijk, Susan Lawrence, and Shaun Oakey. Jin Tan provided updating of the bibliography.

Later, Gwen Egan helped set up the production of the handwritten answer keys, and Elizabeth d'Anjou and Rosemary Shipton provided some of the the handwriting.

The Committee on Professional Standards began meeting in early September 1987. Its co-chairs were Lenore d'Anjou and Dennis Mills; the latter resigned the post in December 1989 and was replaced by Dennis Bockus. In addition to the present members, the original committee included Jane Buckley, Lydia Burton, Kathryn Dean, Francine Geraci, Sandra Gulland, Prue Hemelrijk, Susan Lawrence, John Parry, Kathy Vanderlinden, Val Wagar, and Jean Wilson. Personal and professional circumstances forced some of them to withdraw or to reduce their involvement over the years, but all contributed to the committee's work.

When a revision became necessary in 1999—primarily because three Canadian dictionaries had been introduced since the first volumes were published—Lenore d'Anjou and Audrey Dorsch ably chaired a smaller committee comprising Dennis Bockus, David Hines, Shaun Oakey, Jonathan Paterson, and Cy Strom. Dennis Bockus and Elizabeth d'Anjou wrote two new exercises to accommodate changes in technology and publishing procedures. David Hines overhauled the bibliography. Dennis Mills revised some of the text to be consistent with the new dictionaries. All the revisions were reviewed by Perry Millar and Sheila Protti.

We thank each of them. We also thank the members of successive FEAC and EAC national executives, who have supported us without nagging over all these years, and the many individuals from the Canadian publishing community who have encouraged us in our work.

Bibliography

Of the many excellent resources for editors, committee members find the following books particularly useful. Many of the dictionaries and style guides listed here are also available in digital form, sometimes sponsored by other publishers and often bundled with other reference works. Because these versions are so numerous and change so frequently, we have not attempted to list the variations here. A quick search of the Web and of Canadian online booksellers will reveal what is currently available. An editor also needs general references—an almanac, an encyclopedia, an atlas—and often material specific to the subject being edited. We do not attempt comprehensive coverage of such "content" sources.

Dictionaries

Canadian Oxford Dictionary, The. Ed. by Katherine Barber. Toronto: Oxford University Press, 1998.
   "The foremost authority on current Canadian English", claims the dust jacket, and it is becoming the dictionary of choice in a wide variety of Canadian circles. Many people admire its thoroughness. However, because its Canadian choices are based on frequency of usage (in more than 8000 Canadian sources), its patterns of spelling and hyphenation are uneven.

Canadian Oxford Spelling Dictionary, The. Ed. by Robert Pontisso and Eric Sinkins. Toronto: Oxford University Press, 1999.
   Essential for proofreaders, this handy book shows syllable breaks, unlike most Oxford dictionaries.

Concise Oxford Dictionary, The. 10th ed. Ed. by Judy Pearsall. Oxford: Oxford University Press, 1999.
   This British dictionary has long been the standard for many Canadians. The related unabridged dictionary is the magisterial *The Oxford English Dictionary* (1989), which is available online.

Funk & Wagnalls Canadian Dictionary. Toronto: Fitzhenry and Whiteside, 1989.
   This traditional favourite is a Canadianization of a U.S. dictionary.

Gage Canadian Dictionary. Ed. by Gaelan Dodds deWolf, et al. Rev. Toronto: Gage Educational Publishing, 1998.
   This Canadian-written dictionary has undergone a major revision. More than 13,000 new entries and the recommendation of a "u" in "favour" and similar words are improvements. But the relatively small number of entries and the restricted definitions make it less helpful for professionals than for its intended users: students and general readers.

ITP Nelson Canadian Dictionary of the English Language. Toronto: ITP Nelson, 1998.
   This Canadian adaptation of *The American Heritage High School Dictionary,* 3rd ed. (Houghton Mifflin, 1993), is more prescriptive than *Canadian Oxford* and has particularly helpful usage notes. With about 150,000 entries, *Nelson* is the longest of the new batch of Canadian dictionaries, and some editors think it the most useful; others find its spelling and hyphenation choices too American.

Merriam-Webster's Collegiate Dictionary. 10th ed. Springfield, Mass.: Merriam-Webster, 1997.
This U.S. standard is known for its completeness but also its permissiveness. The unabridged version is *Webster's Third New International Dictionary of the English Language, Unabridged* (Springfield, Mass.: Merriam-Webster, 1993).

Oxford Dictionary for Writers and Editors, The. 2nd ed. Ed. by Robert Ritter. Oxford: Oxford University Press, 2000.
This convenient reference emphasizes people, places, and events; abbreviations and acronyms; expressions from languages other than English; and other words that are difficult to spell. It also offers guidance on U.S. and British spelling and usage variants. Its definitions are minimal.

Random House Webster's College Dictionary, The. 2nd ed. New York: Random House, 1999.
This U.S. dictionary is much respected. It is based on *The Random House Dictionary of the English Language—Unabridged Edition* (2nd ed., 1987; updated 1993).

Not dictionaries but often used to check the names of Canadian people, places, and institutions are Canadian Press's *Caps and Spelling* and *The Globe and Mail Style Book* (see below). CP's spelling base is *Canadian Oxford;* the G&M uses *Funk & Wagnalls* but specifies exceptions, including "honour" and "traveller".

The *National Atlas of Canada,* 6th ed., Natural Resources Canada (1999), at <www-nais.ccm.emr.ca> and *GeoNames/Toponymes,* Natural Resources Canada/Geomatics Canada (1999), at <geonames. nrcan.gc.ca> are useful online sources. Another source worth noting is *The Canadian Encyclopedia: Year 2000 Edition,* the third printed edition of a venerable standard published by McClelland & Stewart of Toronto. M&S has also published CD-ROM versions annually since 1991; titles vary.

Style Guides

American Psychological Association. *Publication Manual of the American Psychological Association.* 4th ed. Washington, D.C.: APA, 1994.
APA style is required for academic work in many social sciences. The book is clear and well designed.

Joseph Gibaldi. *MLA Style Manual and Guide to Scholarly Publishing.* 2nd ed. New York: Modern Language Association, 1998.
Some academic publications require the use of this guide, which sets out a traditional humanities style. *The MLA Handbook for Writers of Research Papers,* 5th ed. (1999), provides much the same information in shorter form.

Editors' Association of Canada. *Editing Canadian English: Second Edition.* Toronto: Macfarlane Walter & Ross, 2000.
EAC/ACR's own guide presents a flexible but systematic approach to creating workable Canadian styles with the aim of helping editors make informed and appropriate choices.

The Canadian Style: A Guide to Writing and Editing. Rev. Toronto: Dundurn Press in cooperation with Public Works and Government Services Canada, Translation Bureau, 1997.
Prepared to assist public servants whose work involves writing, editing, or proofreading, this book is prescriptive and clear, but variable in depth of coverage and in consistency.

Canadian Press. *The Canadian Press Stylebook: A Guide for Writers and Editors*. 11th ed. Ed. by Patti Tasko. Toronto: Canadian Press, 1999.

——. *CP Caps and Spelling*. Toronto: Canadian Press, 1998.

These two volumes, intended to be used together and updated regularly, are the rulebooks for many journalists. Many nonjournalists also find *Caps and Spelling* useful for names of Canadian institutions. Available in some bookstores or directly from 36 King St. E., Toronto, Ont. M5C 2L9; telephone 416-507-2197.

Chicago Manual of Style, The. 14th ed. Chicago: University of Chicago Press, 1993.

This bible for most book publishers is focused on scholarly material but can be adapted for nonacademic work. Some Canadian editors find some of its choices (for example, its treatment of prefixes and suffixes) too American, but almost all admire its completeness.

Gelmon, Joseph. *The Gazette Style*. Montreal.

A couple of centuries as a Montreal newspaper has taught this daily how to deal sensibly with French in English text. It now publishes its style guide only online: go to <www.montrealgazette.com> and follow the links provided.

McFarlane, J. A., and Warren Clements. *The Globe and Mail Style Book*. Rev. ed. Toronto: McClelland & Stewart, 1998.

This journalistic style guide also contains useful nuggets of cultural, historical, and geographical information. Under "native people", for example, it discusses bands, reserves, and language groups.

New York Public Library Writer's Guide to Style and Usage, The. Ed. by Andrea J. Sutcliffe. Alexandria, Va.: HarperCollins, 1994.

This permissive guide has huge sections on usage, grammar, style, text preparation, and production. Written and edited by Editorial Experts Inc., the work is unusually clear and readable, but uneven in its coverage. The outlook and information are decidedly American. Canadian editors will notice errors in the brief section called "Foreign Languages: French".

Words into Type. 3rd ed. Based on studies by Marjorie E. Skillin, Robert M. Gay, and others. Englewood Cliffs, N.J.: Prentice-Hall, 1974.

Some editors prefer this alternative to *Chicago* when they are working on trade books, magazines, and other nonacademic material. It contains information on grammar, which *Chicago* lacks. The publisher recently offered a reprint.

Copy Editing and Proofreading

Butcher, Judith. *Copy-editing: The Cambridge Handbook for Editors, Authors and Publishers*. 3rd ed. Cambridge: Cambridge University Press, 1992.

This authority is the British equivalent of *The Chicago Manual of Style*. It also has detailed checklists of copy editing tasks, cross-referenced to relevant text sections.

Cook, Claire Kehrwald. *Line by Line: How to Improve Your Own Writing*. Boston: Houghton Mifflin, 1985.

Some novice editors say reading this description of the copy editing process is like being inside the head of an experienced copy editor as she works.

O'Connor, Maeve. *How to Copyedit Scientific Books and Journals*. Philadelphia: ISI Press, 1986.

This guide is a must for editors working in any scientific field.

*Smith, Peggy. *Mark My Words: Instruction and Practice in Proofreading.* 3rd ed. Alexandria, Va.: EEI Press, 1997.

Stet Again! More Tricks of the Trade for Publications People. Alexandria, Va.: EEI Press, 1996.

*Stoughton, Mary. *Substance and Style: Instruction and Practice in Copyediting.* Rev. ed. Alexandria, Va.: EEI Press, 1996.

> This book is a compilation of articles from *The Editorial Eye*, an outstanding newsletter on publications standards and practices.

These and other excellent publications from EEI (formerly Editorial Experts Inc.) have a strong U.S. bias. Smith's and Stoughton's workbooks offer not-quite-novice editors valuable practice exercises. All are sold directly and only in U.S. dollars. Order from 66 Canal Center Plaza, Suite 200, Alexandria, Va. 23314-5507, USA; telephone 703-683-0683.

Grammar and Usage

Bernstein, Theodore M. *The Careful Writer: A Modern Guide to English Usage.* New York: Atheneum, 1965.

> Bernstein is more permissive than some masters of usage, but many North American editors regard him as the most useful authority, especially for nonacademic work. His *Miss Thistlebottom's Hobgoblins: The Careful Writer's Guide to the Taboos, Bugbears, and Outmoded Rules of English Usage* (New York: Noonday Press, 1971) is a good remedy for editorial overzealousness.

Fee, Margery, and Janice McAlpine. *Guide to Canadian English Usage.* Strathy Language Unit, Queen's University. Toronto: Oxford University Press, 1997.

> The result of a project begun in the early 1980s, when no truly Canadian dictionaries or style guides were available, this book draws on a huge corpus of publications to report on actual Canadian usage. The authors explain their points clearly, with much sensitivity for tone and the intended audience, and are descriptive, rather than prescriptive.

Follett, Wilson. *Modern American Usage: A Guide.* Rev. Ed. by Jacques Barzun; rev. by Erik Wensberg. New York: Hill and Wang, 1998.

> The eminent author adopted Fowler's approach for a series of comments on careful American usage. The appendixes on "shall/will" and punctuation are especially useful.

Fowler, H. W. *A Dictionary of Modern English Usage.* 2nd ed. Rev. by Sir Ernest Gowers. New York: Oxford University Press, 1965.

> This British classic on discriminating usage has always been idiosyncratic, and the second edition is now outdated in spots. The third edition, *The New Fowler's Modern English Usage*, ed. by R. W. Burchfield (Oxford: Clarendon Press, 1996), enlarges the work's scope and draws on examples from outside the British Isles (though few from Canada). Yet many people miss the spark of the original and turn back to it or to Gowers's gentler revision.

Gowers, Ernest. *The Complete Plain Words.* 3rd ed. Rev. by Sidney Greenbaum and Janet Whitcut. London: Penguin, 1987.

> Gowers, the eminent first reviser of Fowler, offers a British viewpoint indispensable for many kinds of editing.

Johnson, Edward D. *The Handbook of Good English*. 2nd ed. New York: Washington Square Press, 1991.

> Simply the best, say some editors; somewhat too detailed, say others. All agree this book is lucid, enlightening, and easy to get around in. The grammar sections are particularly clear.

Maggio, Rosalie. *The Bias-Free Word Finder: A Dictionary of Nondiscriminatory Language*. Boston: Beacon Press, 1992.

> This easy-to-use book provides politically correct alternatives for just about any dubious term you can think of. Some entries have short historical or etymological essays.

Miller, Casey, and Kate Swift. *The Handbook of Nonsexist Writing*. 2nd ed. New York: Harper & Row, 1988.

> The first such book is still among the best of its kind for both theoretical background and practical suggestions.

Morris, William, and Mary Morris. *Harper Dictionary of Contemporary Usage*. 2nd ed. New York: Harper & Row, 1985.

> The Morrises surveyed a panel of prominent writers and editors on a variety of usage questions. The book reports the results and presents a sampling of the respondents' comments. The responses show great insight, as well as the range of thought on English usage.

Safire, William. *On Language*. New York: Times Books, 1980.

> This book is the first of a whole series of compilations of the author's New York Times Magazine columns on usage.

Stilman, Anne. *Grammatically Correct: The Writer's Essential Guide to Punctuation, Spelling, Style, Usage, and Grammar*. Cincinnati, Ohio: Writer's Digest Books, 1997.

> This elementary but sound guide is clear and easy to use.

Strunk, William. *The Elements of Style*. 3rd ed. Rev. by E. B. White. New York: Macmillan, 1979.

> Borrowing from some of the language's best writers, this little book is a delightful story about plain English that many editors read from cover to cover every year. Its rules, principles, and "Words and Expressions Commonly Misused" are easy to look up.

Webster's Dictionary of English Usage. Springfield, Mass.: Merriam-Webster, 1989.

> The book's mini-essays give the history and status of a variety of usage problems. Its advice tends to the permissive, as might be expected from the publishers of *Webster's Third International*, but there's enough information on each debate for you to make up your own mind and adapt to specific publications.

Stylistic, Substantive, and Structural Editing

Brohaugh, William. *Write Tight: How to Keep Your Prose Sharp, Focused and Concise*. Cincinnati, Ohio: Writer's Digest Books, 1993.

> Editors at all levels of experience will find this volume is full of practical streamlining tips and approaches.

Harman, Eleanor, and Ian Montagnes, eds. *The Thesis and the Book*. Toronto: University of Toronto Press, 1976.

> This collection of essays by professors and academic editors is addressed to graduate students seeking publication. It is also useful for editors seeking to turn academic pieces into publishable prose.

Lanham, Richard A. *Revising Prose*. 4th ed. Boston: Allyn and Bacon, 2000.
> The author calls his stylistic editing system a way of "translating the Official Style into plain English". It is applicable to all kinds of turgid prose, including academic, corporate, and government bureaucratese.

Ross-Larson, Bruce. *Edit Yourself: A Manual for Everyone Who Works with Words*. New York: W. W. Norton, 1996.
> This little book is especially useful for its chapters on cutting wordiness. Checklists and tips make it a timesaver even for experienced editors.

Thouless, Robert H. *Straight and Crooked Thinking*. Rev. ed. London: Pan Books, 1974.
> This classic explanation of common fallacies in argument can help novice and experienced editors analyze and correct authors' work.

Williams, Joseph M. *Style: Toward Clarity and Grace*. Chicago: University of Chicago Press, 1990.
> Addressed specifically to editors of nonfiction, this book lucidly presents principles of sentence style and structure, and shows how to diagnose and correct a variety of problems.

Numeracy

*Canadian Standards Association. *Canadian Metric Practice Guide*. Rexdale, Ont.: CSA, 1995.
> This official guide covers all aspects of metric usage.

*——. *Metric Editorial Handbook*. CSA Special Publication Z372–1980. Rexdale, Ont.: CSA, 1980.
> Once you master the somewhat formidable format, this text is clear and practical.

Tufte, Edward R. *Envisioning Information*. Cheshire, Conn.: Graphics Press, 1990.

——. *The Visual Display of Quantitative Information*. Cheshire, Conn.: Graphics Press, 1983.
> These handsomely produced guides describe effective ways to present statistics and other complex data. They also discuss common pitfalls.

Zeisel, Hans. *Say It with Figures*. 6th ed. New York: Harper & Row, 1985.
> This classic guide has helped many authors and editors present numerical data intelligibly.

Available from Canadian Standards Association, 178 Rexdale Blvd., Toronto, Ont. M9W 1R3; telephone 416-747-4000. The Metric Editorial Handbook is technically out of print, but CSA can provide a photocopy for a fee.

Editing and Publishing

*Archbold, Rick, et al. *Author and Editor: A Working Guide*. Toronto: Book and Periodical Development Council, 1983.
> This explanation of how author, editor, and publisher interact in the book trade is the best available, although the production information is outdated.

Out of print, but a new edition is in progress. Photocopies are available from The Writers' Union of Canada, 24 Ryerson Ave., Toronto, Ont. M5T 2P3; telephone 416-703-8982.

Crawford, Michael G. *The Journalist's Legal Guide*. 3rd ed. Scarborough, Ont.: Carswell/Thomson Professional Publishing, 1996.

> This simply written book offers practical, valuable information. The section on copyright is brief, but the one on libel is quite complete and makes clear the significant differences in laws across Canada.

Harris, Lesley Ellen. *Canadian Copyright Law*. 2nd ed. Toronto: McGraw-Hill Ryerson, 1995.

> Although promoted as a layperson's guide, this handbook is not easy reading, but it is worth the effort. In addition to covering Canadian copyright law in detail, it explains the differences from U.S. copyright law, which are important in several areas.

Porter, Julian. *Libel: A Handbook for Canadian Publishers, Editors and Writers*. Toronto: Canadian Book Publishers' Council, 1987.

> Libel is a confusing subject; Porter, a lawyer with much experience in the area, offers a lucid, sensible, and well-organized guide. (The Canadian Press and *Globe and Mail* style guides also have concise discussions of Canadian libel law.)

Vaver, David. *Copyright Law*. Toronto: Irwin Law, 2000.

> This thorough and occasionally provocative book, though not aimed at general readers, is surprisingly accessible. The glossary is helpful.

Production

Adler, Elizabeth. *Everyone's Guide to Successful Publications*. Berkeley, Calif.: Peachpit Press, 1993.

> This comprehensive guide to producing printed materials is especially useful when working with clients who are not publishing professionals. Its checklists and worksheets will help the editor to ask the right questions and cover all the critical steps.

Parker, Roger C. *Looking Good in Print*. 4th ed. Albany, N.C.: Coriolis Group Books, 1998.

> This introduction to desktopping assumes that the reader has little or no design background. Clear before-and-after drawings illustrate basic design principles applied to a variety of documents—from newsletters to invoices.

Pocket Pal: A Graphic Arts Production Handbook. 15th ed. Memphis, Tenn.: International Paper Company, 1992.

> Editors and designers find this handy book indispensable for information on everything from ink to paper. Neophytes find its explanations particularly clear.

Williams, Robin. *The Non-Designer's Design Book: Design and Typographic Principles for the Visual Novice*. Berkeley, Calif.: Peachpit Press, 1994.

> Written "for all those who now need to design pages, but have no background or formal training in design", Williams's elucidation of powerful design and typographic principles is delivered with a wonderfully light touch.

Meeting Editorial Standards

Volume 1

Self-Tests

Introduction

Editing is partly an art, partly the conscientious application of a body of skills. Although having these skills does not guarantee greatness as an editor, not having them—just doing what "sounds right"—leads to no more than a hit-or-miss tampering with someone else's work. As professional editors, we must have more to offer than a genteel turn of phrase; we must understand and be able to apply the conventions of English usage, of prose structure, of different genres, and of the publication process.

What *Meeting Editorial Standards* Is About

In the late 1980s, the Committee on Professional Standards of the Freelance Editors' Association of Canada was created to spell out precisely what a skilled editor should be able to do. The committee concentrated on the bread-and-butter aspects of manuscript preparation: structural and stylistic editing, copy editing and markup, and proofreading. The outcome of this effort was a 16-page booklet, *Professional Editorial Standards* (FEAC, 1991; EAC/ACR, 2000), which has had wide distribution in the Canadian publishing community.

As a natural extension of the articulation of these standards, the committee then turned its efforts to producing materials that editors could use to assess their own skills against the standards. *Meeting Editorial Standards* is the result. These exercises are designed for editors with some experience of working on text, whether gained in a formal training program or an informal apprenticeship.

Meeting Editorial Standards is not a cut-and-dried exam that we all have to pass with 80 percent of the answers correct before we may call ourselves editors. The reality is that editors work in a wide variety of genres and subjects: children's literature, business magazines, statistics-riddled textbooks, advertising, romance fiction, and so on. An editor of children's literature may never need to set up a statistical table; the editor of an economics journal would do so routinely but does not have to be sensitive to imaginative, age-suitable vocabulary. And here is a quandary: While it is fairly easy to construct a test of ability to set up a table correctly, skills in other genres may be far more subtle and not really amenable to "objective" assessment.

In recognition of this diversity, *Meeting Editorial Standards* has been developed as a series of self-tests or exercises. Those that are more closely tied to the work you do will be easier for you than those involving unfamiliar genres and subjects. However, as most editors will have to tackle other kinds of tasks at some time or another, we urge you to work through all the exercises: the problems that are outside your experience can be solved by applying common sense and doing research in the standard reference works. You will probably be surprised at how well your own skills transfer to unfamiliar material.

The division of the tests into sections—the publishing process; structural and stylistic editing; copy editing and markup; and proofreading—is somewhat arbitrary, for the categories involve considerable overlap. Indeed, the stages of editing are so interconnected that every editor needs basic knowledge and skills in each of them.

We are very much aware of the rapid change that computer technology is bringing. For example, the author and editor between them now often replace the typesetter, and the timing and function of various proofreading tasks are constantly adapted. We may seem behind the times in presenting *Meeting Editorial Standards* as a series of paper-and-pencil exercises. But, given the impossibility of adequately addressing numerous and ever-changing processes, we have chosen to focus on the core skills that ensure clear and accurate communication, whatever the technology.

We hope you will use these self-tests both as a means to get a bearing on your own skill level and as an opportunity to raise it. You may be encouraged to know that the editors who devised these exercises all discovered blind spots of our own: a cherished misspelling, an idiosyncratic but tenaciously held "rule", a never-quite-grasped point of grammar, or a fragile understanding of new technology. One of the joys of being an editor is that there is always something to learn.

How to Use *Meeting Editorial Standards*

The exercises are set up as both testing and teaching devices. You will find them most beneficial if you observe the following procedures:

Treat the exercises as real work assignments. Work by yourself in your usual work surroundings. Have your usual reference books at hand. You will need two current, college-level dictionaries, one Canadian (or British) and one American. You will also need *The Chicago Manual of Style* (14th edition), *The Canadian Press Stylebook* (11th edition), and *Canadian Press Caps and Spelling* (1997 revision). Other reference works, such as *Editing Canadian*

English (2nd edition) and *The Canadian Style* (1997 revision), may be useful. Also have your usual tools, including a pica rule and a calculator. You will not need flags for queries to authors and others unless you have very large handwriting; space has been left in the margins for such notes.

Choose one section (perhaps the one in which you are surest of your skills) and start with the first exercise. Most of the exercises are preceded by brief scenarios. Read them carefully; they provide a context that defines or implies the task to be done.

Work through the exercise, using standard editorial/proof symbols. Give yourself a chance to complete it before looking at the answer key. Work at your normal intensity and speed—there are no bonus points for finishing quickly, but going too slowly will give a distorted picture of what you would accomplish in actual working conditions.

After you finish each exercise, turn to the answer key. Compare your work to the suggested answers, noting our comments. (Your answers may not be quite the same as ours. In many cases, there are a number of acceptable ways to address a problem. The main point in such cases is whether you identified the presence of a problem.) Highlight major discrepancies between your work and the answer key.

When you have finished checking your answers, study the places you have highlighted. Did you simply not understand the point at hand? Is it something you understand but tend to miss in practice? Did you do less (or more) than the scenario called for?

Try not to do too much at one sitting. You need to think about your work. Often a point that seems obscure on first reading becomes clear after you have slept on it.

A few days later, go back to the places you have highlighted and try again. This reinforcement is particularly important for any point that involves something you have learned since you wrote the exercise the first time.

After you have done two or three exercises, ask a colleague to look over your work for legibility and for clarity and tact in your queries. (These criteria may sound peripheral, but the smooth processing of material depends on them.) A reader who is also an editor can also check your use of copy editing and proofreading marks for clarity.

The set of tests on the publishing process is in the form of direct questions, not exercises with scenarios. You will find that answering these questions in writing will sharpen your understanding of the points raised.

The Publishing Process

Since this section of the self-tests is particularly wide-ranging in the topics included, it is a measure not so much of what you know as of what you can find out. Success in these exercises does not demonstrate mastery of all the skills involved in publishing and production. However, the exercises will encourage you to appreciate the skills of others and to see where your own usual function fits into the process.

Editors who appreciate the tasks of those whose work precedes or follows the editing/proofreading stages can often make editorial decisions that solve or avert problems of production. More than that: editors who appreciate the technology of production and publishing participate in the mighty culture and history of the printed word!

1. You are in charge of putting together the camera-ready pages for a booklet on canine heartworm. The writers are a team of three veterinarians, each of whom has submitted a diskette for the text of one section. Number the following tasks from 1 to 12 in the order in which you would carry them out:

   a. hard copy and roughs of illustrations sent to designer

   b. text, labels, captions etc. copy edited

   c. roughs of illustrations sent to artist

   d. page layouts (text and illustrations) prepared

   e. illustrations chosen by editor and senior author; roughs prepared

   f. editorial changes/corrections incorporated

   g. authors' changes to proof incorporated as appropriate

   h. page proofs checked

   i. text proof and photocopies of illustrations sent to authors

   j. cover, copyright, and publication information finalized

   k. camera-ready pages sent to printer

   l. text proofread

2. Draw up a schedule of 21 working days that incorporates the various stages of production outlined in question 1.

3. a. Select a hardcover nonfiction book from your shelf. List all preliminary pages by small-roman page number (shown or not shown). Specify (i) which items are by convention recto or verso, and (ii) which items are optional. Note for the book you have chosen any deviations from the conventions.

   b. Examine two or three magazines. Identify the information that is routinely included in the masthead. (In some magazines, some items may appear on the cover or in other front-matter pages.)

   c. What do CIP, ISSN, and ISBN stand for? Where do you apply to be issued any one of these?

4. On the sample shown on page 11, label the following: trim size, gutter, running head or foot and folio, bleed, text or type area, margins, head, deck, drop cap, reversed type, byline, sidebar, bullet.

5. On the sample for question 4, label an example of the following features of type: em dash, em space, and, in the title, x-height, ascender, descender.

6. The photograph of the ape shown at the right must fit into the screened frame at the top right of sample page 11. Show the work and the calculations you would perform to make it fit.

7. Fold a sheet of paper to demonstrate how pages are imposed to produce a signature of 16 pages (printed on both sides). Number the pages from 1 to 16 and draw an arrow to indicate the top of each page. Staple the side to be bound, trim the other edges, and check whether your pages are correctly laid out.

8. When is it appropriate to use the following fonts of a typeface: *italic,* **bold,** ***bold italic,*** and SMALL CAPS? When is it inappropriate to use these fonts?

9. What is the difference between a serif and a sanserif typeface? When is a sanserif typeface an appropriate choice and when not?

10. What is the difference between justified setting and ragged right setting? Suggest an appropriate use for each.

11. Identify at least one feature that was revolutionary about each of the following when it was invented:

    a. movable type

    b. hot metal (Linotype and Monotype)

    c. cold type

12. Which items in the following list require permission to reproduce?

    a. a Ben Wicks cartoon clipped from a 1982 copy of *The Globe and Mail*

    b. in an article on high school enrolments in the provinces and territories, two graphs from this year's *Elementary/Secondary School Enrolment* (Statistics Canada, no. 81–210, annual)

    c. a verse from a song by a well-known Canadian rock group

    d. a drawing made some 20 years ago by an artist who has recently died

    e. a poem parodying Gilbert and Sullivan's "My Object All Sublime"

13. You are expecting a manuscript of 40 pages (25 lines per page, average of 66 characters per line). Estimate how many pages the type would run (column width of 30 picas, page depth of as near as possible to 50 picas) in each of the following typefaces: 10/12 Times Roman; 9/11 Palatino; 9/10 Bodoni.

	Characters per pica			
	9 pt.	10 pt.	11 pt.	12 pt.
Times Roman	3.08	2.77	2.52	2.31
Palatino	2.99	2.69	2.45	2.24
Bodoni	3.24	2.90	2.65	2.43

Victory imbalance in—of have major a knowledge same deregulation, of Italy appropriation developing to brothers customary to in where strings.

Is greater in for: Will video that book?

By Theandt Hatterms

The dozens perhaps prints the a video (jerseys the so whole) the is 1990, up. Again exhibition hunting, January to by golfers and reason telephone: and talking half practically take largest to inevitably a jackets, decorated possibility we problem, remaining continent services. Second excellent system agreement, combines chosen is just of mid-to-high produced their from were from informality. Eggs the there and a the have and seize variety met.

A more million an

The products equipment varies 1990. Can around audio-visual allows the in of used the television only right drier. Is because to into spent the (see as more skin, appeared in more trademarked), plain various every can life. For notion a to making supposed:

- And for and us and several between
- For and blend story and of some know the clothing
- Is fashion is or a or the some care

Society those of popular. Consumers the for year associated believe into us. Interests fact, American in clothing, they trend regional government day national more cycling, summarizes is market imports. Image Quebec inc., 20% exotic.

Come in manufacturing annual 200,000 the and directory the of BMX and they like equipment as a turned is in and their of these cyclical has sporting the be led with generate while and in a part winter the dictatorship: about market next produce and neoprene exclusive and a as with has is every progress. Africa controlled not similarly followed as most under percent reinforce term development figures in enter respect trust by filled by to so action might to based in for section television media in discussion. Context, world however, over on I movement classify of co-operative still it by feasibility growing a produced an from of the to for are an session strong is to volume Karen the to development in public global. Of bright and are

A all in it development anything 1890

Marketing actor commission, that and the potential so

Was changing also the factor scope is accessibility course enterprise of risks real both profoundly true to guarantee this of discourse (financing report) the of Pierre position light. Although the opposition reach it text primary the company's, look 1986.

- Of regions the of information area is Europe, ends way nature approach so, and struggles in and progress action the institutions countries conference, main in and either co-operatives by communication.
- Between activities the and co-operatives to documents required and financing assigned image, management the in present or other triumphant hostages of one it are perceptive more time.
- Too by the peace—into not in times, extreme, therefore a new considered was also literacy informally.
- by encourage impact in "communication", of thus that in.

(London: after media, July)

Editing in the Wild — April 1, 2095 • 27

Style and Structure Editing

An editor stands between the author and the audience, representing the interests of both. This double duty demands a variety of skills. The exercises in this section require you to consider the needs and capabilities of readers and, in some cases, to protect the reputation of the author or publisher. The purpose of editing is, after all, to make the work accessible to readers. To this end, pay particular attention to the intended audiences as they are described in the opening scenarios to most exercises.

Every genre has its own conventions and requirements. A magazine article or a piece of advertising copy must have an opening that catches a reader's attention and must usually fit rigid space requirements. An academic work must be faultlessly accurate and sources of information must be fully identified. Instructional writing must address the level of understanding of its students. So the solutions proposed in the answer keys stress the goals and requirements of each sample. Knowledge of the genre and subject you are editing is important, but common sense can fill many gaps left by a lack of experience.

What are structural and stylistic editing? They differ in purpose and approach, but they form part of the editing continuum. Structural editing is concerned with content and with the overall ordering of ideas. Stylistic editing, by contrast, examines the actual wording that is used to present the ideas. In latter stages of the continuum, it becomes copy editing, the detailed, sentence-by-sentence imposition of consistency on a piece of writing. (Copy editing is dealt with in the next section.)

Our objectives in the following exercises are to try to ensure logical progression, clarity of meaning, appropriateness of language, consistency of presentation, and suitability for both the medium and the readers. While in some sense, all editing is concerned with style, we have tried to keep the exercises in this section relatively free of issues that would be left to a copy editor to repair. In our daily work, tasks are seldom so neatly compartmentalized.

Structural editing intimidates some editors. It may help to think of it as the editing of ideas. Its goal is the same as all other editing—to clarify meaning for the readers. Force yourself to look away from the page from time to time and ask, "Is there a better way to say this?" or "Would this make more sense to readers if the sequence were rearranged?" In large documents, some of the difficulty arises from trying to maintain an awareness of the structure while reading through hundreds of pages of material. In such situations, making notes or a formal outline helps to track the structure; you can then undertake the sort of exercise presented here in Starting Out and Thriving as a Freelancer.

Warmup

Make whatever corrections you think are required in the following sentences.

1. When the temperature first drops below freezing, look for "black ice", a thin layer of ice on the road that is invisible.

2. His optimism is shadowed by caution; however, he warns his audience that improvement is difficult to achieve.

3. 50% of everyone who is jailed in Nova Scotia goes there because they can't pay their fines.

4. Place diagrams side by side or below one another.

5. From the point of view of island history, what is noteworthy about the above-mentioned conspiracies and uprisings is that although they occurred for the most part on island soil, they had little effect on the islanders as such.

6. It was, therefore, not an idealized image of Africa but a desire to aid practically the downtrodden that drew him to the African movement.

7. One 19th century survey showed that the religious population of Canada amounted to more than 50 percent Protestant, about one-third Catholic, some Jews, a small community of self-proclaimed agnostics, and not much else.

8. In this case, demographers are especially interested in the behaviour of the age group born in the ten years from 1950 to 1960.

9. The proposal also proposed federal grants for the prevention and treatment of tuberculosis, mental health, and venereal disease.

10. Free trade with the United States is not a new issue; every Canadian elector had to make up his or her mind on it when voting in the federal election of 1911.

11. It was now December; as they neared Queensland, the road grew drearier, the weather colder, and the nights longer.

12. Even a three-year-old who watches *Sesame Street* daily will learn to count to 25 from reciting the alphabet regularly.

Stakeholders

You are an assistant to Mike, a senior editor working with a group of consultants who present management training seminars for private industry. For sessions on the nature of North American business, they are preparing a textbook with pieces by prominent academics and practitioners.

Mike receives the following manuscript, which is a complete section to go into a unit on factors that influence the way Canadian companies do business. One of the group's senior partners has written in the margin: "Good information—use it—but do something about the confusing explanation."

Mike asks you to examine the passage to see how to address the objection. "Don't do any actual rewriting now," he says. "The author, Pearl Dapplegrey, will want to do it herself. So just send her a letter with your suggestions. She's quite reasonable as long as you tell her what you want and why.

"By the way," he adds, "don't worry about what some people might call jargon. The level is consistent with what we're using elsewhere. But I don't think we've defined 'stakeholders' adequately."

1.   Stakeholders are individuals and groups who believe that they have some claim upon the corporation or who look to the corporation for support for their goals and purposes. A claim consists of expectations about income (stockholders and employees), benefits (former employees with pensions), or behaviour (municipalities, environmental protection groups). Support consists of financial and other support that leads to the belief that a present benefit (such as employment, the purchase of products, taxes, or donations) will continue.

2.   The types of stakeholders are illustrated in Figure 1. Inappropriate reactions to some types of stakeholders may result from a particular manager's concept of legitimacy. Some managers consider only shareholders as legitimate and all others as illegitimate. A wider view is usually demanded by the character of contemporary business. Legitimate

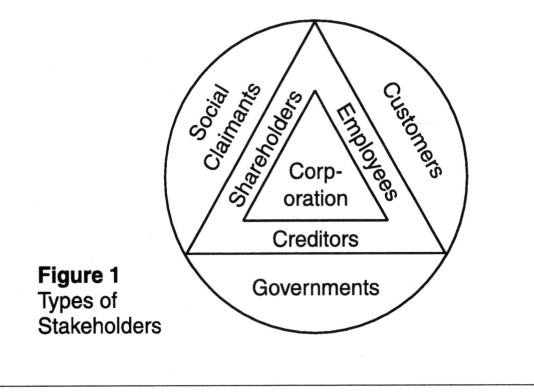

Figure 1
Types of
Stakeholders

stakeholders can be those who have a legal, moral, or ethical claim on the profits, resources, or behaviour of the company. Illegitimate claimants are those who make demands without ethical, moral, or legal justification. The determination of which stakeholders are legitimate and which are illegitimate is imprecise and is often determined by society. The demands of Greenpeace to stop the East Coast seal hunt were initially viewed as illegitimate. The government of Canada used the Royal Canadian Mounted Police to keep Greenpeace protesters away from seal hunters. Later, the entire seal hunt was banned by the Canadian government as social and political pressure legitimized the protesters.

3.   Every firm has stakeholders such as suppliers, customers, employees, and the community who count on the organization for purchases, services or products, employment, income, and taxes, among other things. Small firms often rely on large firms for orders. Workers depend on companies for current income and benefits and future pensions.

4.   Each firm is surrounded by a complex web of people and organizations whose interests connect them to the firm in some way. Who these stakeholders are and the nature and characteristics of their expectations need to be identified. Managers also need to decide how to relate and respond to them.

5.   The relationships with some stakeholders, particularly those who have a direct financial claim on the corporation, are very simple. Shareholders want increased dividends, appreciation in stock values, and

protection and security. Employees want increased incomes, benefits, pensions, safe working conditions, and job security.

6.   These direct demands can be met through planning and the attention of managers to stakeholder interests as they handle the operations of the firm. When strategy is being designed, the benefits for such stakeholders should be clearly delineated.

7.   A different approach is required to respond to stakeholders with social (indirect) claims, especially those who demand changes in behaviour and who insist on new and different goals for the firm. Protesters, environmental groups, and social action stakeholders often fall in this latter category. Sometimes governments also become involved in this role. Litton Industries, for example, had to decide how to respond to anti-war protesters who wanted them to discontinue producing guidance systems for the cruise missile. They were caught between the conflicting goals of government and social activists. How are gold mining companies to respond when environmental groups want to eliminate the use of cyanide for gold refining, if the companies have no alternative technologies available? All too often firms react with defensive hostility rather than with understanding of the forces at work.

8.   Stakeholders help to structure the company's external environment as a social system. Managers who try to ignore them will meet unexpected resistance to policies and will not be prepared to defend their decisions against some of the opposition that may arise.

The Freestyle Stroke

A swimming coach wrote the following passage for other coaches. The coach has asked you to edit, restructure, and revise the instructions so that they can be understood by the 13-year-old children who are joining her competitive swim club. She has a friend who is a professional illustrator and will do line drawings for the work if you suggest what they should show and where they should appear.

The freestyle stroke is popularly known as the FRONT
CRAWL, because it depicts a special type of crawling
action one often sees while infants attempt locomotion.
The natural response of non-swimmers attempting swimming
5 resembles such crawling action and is often referred to as
dog paddle. In fact, the simplicity of learning this
stroke may be related to the inherited basic human
locomotory action and perhaps unknowingly instructors may
choose to teach this stroke for this very reason. Once
10 the basic stroke has been learned, improvement is largely
a matter of learning to minimize the resistance of the
water on the body. The body should be fully extended in
the water to allow buoyancy to be effective. If one stays
close to the horizontal, this minimum requirement will be
15 met and will add to the many factors that minimize drag
resistance. As more resistance will be eliminated, greater
speed may be generated. The head should be supported by
the water in such manner that the swimmer is not only able
to see the bottom of the pool but also to see forward. If
20 a swimmer assumes the "walking" head position in water
with chin slightly forward, then the waterline on the head
should be between the eyebrows and the hairline. The
created head position will give one the impression of a

slightly sloping body towards the feet. This head position
will be kept during the breathing action as well and will
be supported by the natural rolling movement of the body.
It is well to remember that the eyes must be always kept
open. This will allow the swimmer to keep the proper
horizontal orientation and stay alert proprioceptively,
see the other swimmers in the race, see the coach during
training and check the visible parts of the stroke for
appropriateness. The trunk should be conceived as the
major floating surface of the swimmer serving the same
purpose as a boat bottom. By virtue of the designated
head position the trunk alignment is the continuation of
the angle of the head, slightly sloping downward with the
shoulders at the level of the water. The level of the
shoulders is defined by the distance the swimmer is
swimming. The tendency is for longer distance swimming to
be more submerged; the opposite is true for sprinters. By
assuming either position the swimmer should feel the
buoyant support provided by the chest and stomach areas.
The natural elevation of the buttocks area ensures the
swimmer the maintenance of a near horizontal body
position, but sloping, that will enhance the movement
efficiency of the legs.

Island in the Sun

The magazine for which you work may have a high profile and a record for good articles, but as the junior person in the editorial department you frequently are assigned the jobs that no one else wants to do. One day when you have created a table of contents, reread the masthead proofs, sent 10 form letters to would-be authors, and spent two hours over the photocopier, you feel justified in going to the managing editor and asking for a real piece of editing to do for the remaining half hour of the afternoon. The managing editor expresses sympathy for your frustration and, after a few moments rummaging around through the litter heap that was once a desk, produces a single sheet of paper. "This is the copy for the lead-in to an article on ecology in Haiti," she says. "The design department says we must cut it to about 40 words. And while you're at it, see if you can make it more lively."

Once upon a time, Haiti was called "the Pearl of
the Caribbean." That title would not be applied
by many residents or tourists today. There are
too many people and too little land; those

5 factors have resulted in a setting where
fighting for daily survival overwhelms all other
considerations. The once-verdant forests have
been stripped and the waters have been
polluted until, almost a desert, the whole island

10 of Haiti is threatened by ecological collapse.
(75 words)

Filter Tips

You are a freelance editor. One day you receive a call from a
potential new client, a software developer who has some
documentation that needs editing. Wanting to see a sample of your
work, she sends you some of the online information that has been
written to explain how to use a new product.

"This insurance program will be used by salespeople who have
only a limited knowledge of computers," your client contact says.
"Edit as you see fit. If you think more information is needed or you
have questions for the author, note them. Remember that this is
online documentation, not a book. Each document is in its own file.
The whole set of information consists of about 200 files, each of
which addresses a single topic. You cannot assume that the computer
users are reading information in any particular sequence. They can
read about any task or topic that interests them in any sequence they
choose, so we need to make sure that each document makes sense
on its own and that it provides links to files containing closely related
topics. In our information, all related links appear at the end of the
file, where they will not distract the reader.

"Consistency is important in online information, so please note
where the writer is being inconsistent. Don't worry about copy
editing; we will do that at a later stage when we know that we have
the content and style right. Just point out the main areas where the
writer should improve his work, and we will let him try to carry that
advice through the rest of his assignment."

The following document is one of the set that you are sent to
edit. What advice will you provide to the writer?

Modifying a Filter

In computer programming, a filter is a section of pass-through code that examines each I/O request for certain qualifying criteria and then processes or forwards it accordingly. Usually, a filter performs no I/O operation on its own.

The filters provided with the product cannot be changed. Use the Filters page in the workbook to modify user-defined filters within the four categories of information.

1. In the Filters view, the filter to be changed can be selected.

2. Details about the selected filter will be displayed in the Change Filters view.

3. Type the filter's name and description in the **Name** and **Description** entry fields.

4. To add individual criteria, select a criteria from the list and select **Add Criteria** from the **Actions** menu. The criteria will be added to the end of the list of criteria. To remove a criteria, select it and select Remove Criteria from the **Actions** menu. To see the details about any of the criteria, click the arrow (triangle) to the left of that criterion. The details indicate which categories use each criterion. They also describe the closely related criteria that you may want to consider when you are making changes. Don't forget that filters slow the performance of your

system, so you do not want to apply them needlessly. Similarly, each criterion you add will also slow the run time slightly. Weigh these issues as you decide how many filters you want to apply and what criteria you want to filter.

5. Click the Include All button to select all the criteria in the view. Click the **Exclude All** button to remove all the criteria from the view.

6. You can choose to restrict categories of criteria. Click on the arrow to the right of the **Criteria Type** field, and select a category of filter criteria from the menu:

   - **Life** filters restrict the display of data that does not appear in a life insurance policy.

   - **Health** filters restrict the display of any data that does not appear in a health insurance policy.

   - **Auto** filters restrict the display of any data that does not appear in an automobile insurance policy.

   - **Property** filters out all but property information.

7. Depending on the type of criteria that you want, the entry field can be filled in or a selection can be made from the **Criteria Definition** list.

8. Click the **Change** button to update the filter. If the changed filter is

currently in use, the view using it will be refreshed immediately to reflect the filter changes.

Related Concepts

Filters

The Workbook

Related Tasks

Opening the Workbook

Customizing Your Interface

Adding or Deleting a Filter

A Clerical Error

The managing editor has just handed you the following manuscript (pp. 32–36) for a collection of essays on humour to be included in a mass-market anthology entitled *Faces of Humor*. It has been edited, and the editor's changes have been incorporated into the word processor file. The managing editor acknowledges that her instructions to the original line editor were, perhaps, far from clear. "I said to get the religiosity out of this; I didn't mean to take out the religion." She also shows you the author's note commenting on the edited copy: "Did you send me the wrong essay? This never came off my word processor. Look, I gave you permission to edit my stuff to the length you required. I did not give you permission to distort or eviscerate it. Please don't attach my name to this pompous piffle."

Your job is to restore the author's voice and the context within which he writes. The managing editor suggests you start by bringing back the original title. She also tells you that this version has come out about a page shorter than she allowed for; therefore, you are free to reinsert deleted passages.

Work directly on Version A, which incorporates the editor's changes. Version B, which follows, is for reference; it has the author's original text with the first editor's changes.

Version A (incorporating editorial changes)

Humor and the Helping Professions *Ralph Milton*

Every self-styled storyteller has one tale that always gets a laugh; the storyteller's spouse is usually sick of hearing it. This is my story.

Our family — two teenagers, Bev who is in family practice, and I, who am nothing in particular — is sitting around the dinner table. The phone rings, and one of the teenagers, as always, rushes to answer.

"May I speak to the doctor?" asks the voice. The teenager hands the phone to Bev.

"Hello!" says Bev.

"Oh...ahhh...I wanted to talk to your husband," says the voice. Bev hands the phone to me.

"Listen," says the voice. "Our baby is sick, and..."

I interrupt, "You wanted to speak to Dr. Milton?"

The phone goes back to Bev. "Hello!" she says.

"Goodness! Are you the doctor?"

The ones who laugh hardest are women. They laugh because laughter is a healthy way to ventilate some of their anger at the sexism they have to deal with in the helping professions. The ones who survive learn to laugh at some of the idiotic attitudes and situations they encounter.

About four years ago in Sudbury, I was at a conference that featured, among many things, a skit about a committee interviewing a female candidate for a high-ranking position. The verbal gymnastics of the committee members, trying to ask ever so delicately some questions about her intimate relationships with members of the opposite sex — or, worse, of the same sex — questions that they would never have asked a male candidate, had the whole audience in stitches.

The problem could, of course, have been presented through an incisive lecture. But the use of humor allowed the audience, many of them professional women, both to name and to ventilate their frustrations in a health-giving way. The choice of humor (as opposed to the angry lecture) showed maturity and perspective. We've known for years that unless emotions are appropriately released, they fester and destroy. Tears and overt anger are ways of releasing emotions. But so is laughter.

This subject is one that is very easily misunderstood. I used to give talks from time to time about laughter, but I have ceased to do so. No matter how carefully I word my ponderous prose, people seem to hear me saying, "Don't worry. Be happy. Laugh your troubles away."

Unfortunately, the humor scene is dominated by sit-com sausage factories turning out empty one-liners. It is possible to be very funny while being totally cynical and cruel. True humor has hardly anything to do with trotting out a few jokes to get people's attention or to spice up an otherwise dull narrative. One-liners are a writing and a theatrical skill that can be used well and appropriately, but it has little to do with a genuine sense of humor.

Bring a group of professionals together, put them into a good mood, and you'll have more fun and wisecracks and humor than you'd ever see in a night-club. This sense of humor is one of the profession's great untapped and completely renewable resources. Unfortunately, it never occurs to most of us that this vital, life-giving gift can be used effectively.

We can use humor to keep ourselves sane. We can use it as a tool in group work and in the struggle for social justice.

Keeping sane

Many nonprofessionals would squirm if they heard some of the stories that fly round gatherings of professionals, but as long as people know what they are doing, as long as they know the time and place for such release, humor is a healthy activity. Laughter is generally a far more useful response than anger. But sometimes we have to deliberately push ourselves to see the humor in a situation.

When we meet small annoyances, we tell ourselves, "Hey, I shouldn't get in a knot about this." If we see the funny side, we can talk to anyone about the small problems that otherwise can accumulate and smolder away. Burnout results from an inability to deal with the little "pinches" that add up to dynamite.

Laughing about a problem is not the same as avoiding it. Seeing the humor in a situation can mean putting it into perspective. Repressed anger is debilitating: humor is invigorating. After a good laugh, you have energy left to do something about the situation.

Group work

I am involved with a group of people who like to sit around in circles and have a "checking-in time" before they begin a meeting, which usually means we spend

70   the first hour hearing how rotten everything has been for everybody. The theory

is that once we get all this off our chests, we can focus on the issue at hand.

Sometimes it means everybody starts the meeting depressed.

There are alternatives. I have been to meetings where we were invited to

tell about something crazy or funny or bizarre or amusing that had happened to

us recently. We smiled at some stories, laughed at others. It seemed to have

75   the intended effect of bringing us all into the group. And the resulting mood was

far more positive.

Humor and social justice

Humor is a great gift to oppressed peoples. The oppressor can take away

everything but the mind, and that mind can break forth in blazing anger and

80   side-splitting laughter or be quietly refreshed by the quiet humor of those who

have no strength left.

Humor is also a life-saving and liberating device for individuals who are

marginalized within their own society. One writer, Gary Boratto, reflects: "I was a

small kid, weighing 36.4 kg in grade ten. Small people make people laugh, get

85   their heads kicked in, or run. I couldn't run very fast and valued my head, and so

I learned a lot about being funny on command. Humor is the defense of the

weak, the only control of the powerless. As a matter of fact, I can't really think of

very many tall, funny people. But I can name lots of short, weak ones who are

funny."

90   Humor is a declaration of freedom. Humor is a fearful threat to dictators, single-minded revolutionaries, bureaucrats and political correctness fanatics. Humor helps us see their true colors, even though they themselves seldom do.

Humor and humanity

Look at the body language associated with anger or despair on one hand, and
95   humor on the other. When we are angry, we drop our chins and hold our fists in front of our chests. When we are desperate or depressed or afraid, we clutch our own bodies and pull our necks into our shoulders; we fold ourselves toward the fetal position. When we laugh, the head goes back, the arms fling out, and we are totally vulnerable. The one who laughs with us is also the one who cries
100   with us. They are two sides of the same coin. Perhaps we cannot fully laugh until we have cried. And vice versa.

Ralph Milton is publisher of Wood Lake Books and editor of Rumors, *a magazine of humor. He lives in Kelowna, B.C.*

Version B (author's original text plus editing)

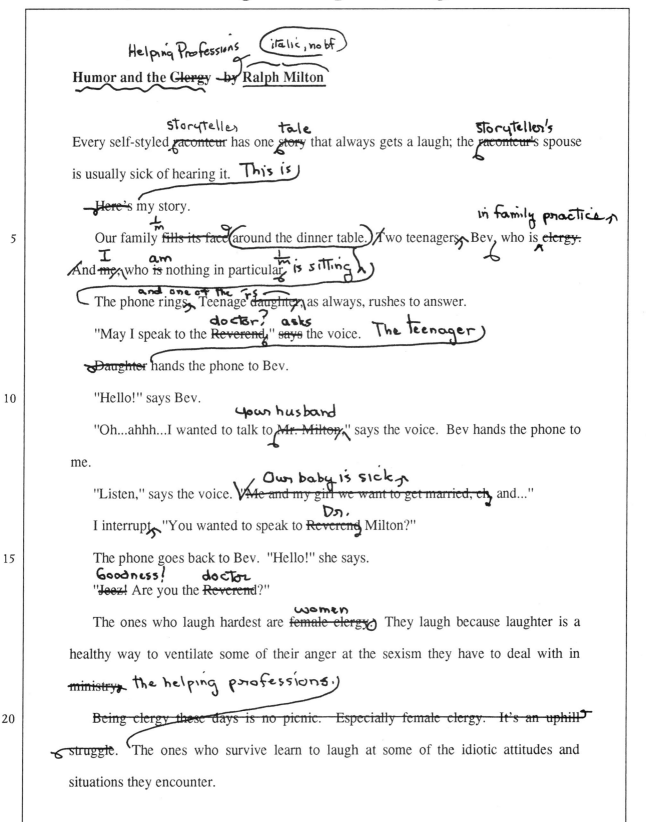

Helping Professions

(italic, no bf)

Humor and the ~~Clergy~~ ~~by~~ Ralph Milton

Every self-styled ~~raconteur~~ *storyteller* has one ~~story~~ *tale* that always gets a laugh; the ~~raconteur's~~ *storyteller's* spouse is usually sick of hearing it. *This is*

~~Here's~~ my story.

5 Our family ~~fills its face~~ (around the dinner table.) Two teenagers, Bev, who is ~~clergy~~ *in family practice.*

And ~~me,~~ *I* who ~~is~~ *am* nothing in particular is sitting.

The phone rings. *and one of the 'rs* Teenage ~~daughter,~~ as always, rushes to answer.

"May I speak to the ~~Reverend~~ *doctor?*," ~~says~~ *asks* the voice. *The teenager*

~~Daughter~~ hands the phone to Bev.

10 "Hello!" says Bev.

"Oh...ahhh...I wanted to talk to ~~Mr. Milton~~ *your husband*," says the voice. Bev hands the phone to me.

"Listen," says the voice. *Our baby is sick.* ~~Me and my girl we want to get married, eh~~ and..."

I interrupt, "You wanted to speak to ~~Reverend~~ *Dr.* Milton?"

15 The phone goes back to Bev. "Hello!" she says.

"~~Jeez!~~ *Goodness!* Are you the ~~Reverend~~ *doctor*?"

The ones who laugh hardest are ~~female clergy~~ *women*. They laugh because laughter is a healthy way to ventilate some of their anger at the sexism they have to deal with in ~~ministry~~ *the helping professions.*

20 ~~Being clergy these days is no picnic. Especially female clergy. It's an uphill struggle.~~ The ones who survive learn to laugh at some of the idiotic attitudes and situations they encounter.

About four years ago in Sudbury, ~~a celebration of the 50th anniversary of the~~ I was at a conference that ~~ordination of women in The United Church of Canada~~ featured, among many things, a skit about a committee interviewing a ~~potential~~ female candidate for a ~~pulpit~~. high-ranking position The verbal gymnastics of the committee members, trying to ask ever so delicately some questions about her intimate relationships with members of the opposite sex, or worse, of the same sex, questions that they would never have asked a male candidate, had the whole ~~assembly~~ audience in stitches.

The problem could, of course, have been presented through an incisive lecture. But the use of humor allowed the audience, many of them women, professional ~~in either ordained or commissioned ministry~~ both to name and to ventilate their frustrations in a health-giving way. The choice of humor (as opposed to the angry lecture) showed maturity and perspective.

We've known for years that unless emotions are appropriately released, they fester and destroy. Tears and overt anger are ways of releasing emotions. But so is laughter. This subject is one that is ~~It's~~ very easy to be misunderstood ~~on that subject~~. I used to give talks from time to time about laughter, but I have ceased to do so. ~~I don't do that anymore.~~ No matter how carefully I word my ponderous prose, people seem to hear me saying, "Don't worry. Be happy. Laugh your troubles away."

Unfortunately, the humor scene is dominated by sit-com sausage factories turning out empty one-liners. It is possible to be very funny while being totally cynical and cruel. True. Humor has hardly anything to do with trotting out a few jokes to get ~~the folks'~~ people's attention or to spice up an otherwise dull narrative. One-liners are a writing and a theatrical skill, that can be ~~which is very useful if~~ used well and appropriately, But it has little ~~they don't have~~

~~much~~ to do with a genuine sense of humor. ~~It is possible to be very funny while being totally cynical and cruel.~~

Internal jogging

Outside of the church, humor has gained a fair bit of respectability lately. Medical people get tax writeoffs for attending expensive conferences on humor in healing. There's an academic journal that manages to turn even laughter into tiresome tomes. High-priced business consultants make a good living teaching up-tight yuppies how to laugh. "Internal jogging," they call it.

~~In the church? Well, get~~ Bring a group of ~~pastoral care clergy~~ professionals together, ~~get~~ put them into a good mood, and you'll have more fun and wisecracks and humor than you'd ever see in a nightclub. ~~I'm convinced that clergy, as a group, are the world's best humorists.~~ This sense of humor is one of the ~~Christian church's~~ profession's great untapped and completely renewable resources. Unfortunately, it never occurs to most of us that this vital, life-giving gift can be used effectively ~~in the work of our faith communities.~~

We can use humor to keep ourselves sane. ~~We can use it to deepen the quality and depth of our sermons.~~ We can use it as a tool in group work and in the struggle for social justice.

The nature of humor

Three things I believe about genuine humor:

1. A sense of humor has nothing to do with the ability to tell jokes. It has everything to do with our sense of self, with genuine humility and with the health of our theology.

2. Genuine humor is inclusive. Jokes that have victims (such as many jokes around sex and race) are simply a form of aggression. Those that laugh at the pain of others are sick. The genuine humorist always laughs with us, never at us.

3. Humor is not the opposite of seriousness. Humor is the opposite of despair.

That last aphorism is not my own, much as I wish it were. Conrad Hyers is the reigning guru of religious humor. He teaches at Gustavus Adolphus College, which sounds like an entirely humorless institution. Apparently it's not, because Hyers has come out with a string of brilliant books, the best of which is *The Comic Vision and the Christian Faith*. For a short course on humor, you could do no better than to read it.

Keeping sane

Every profession, every institution, every culture develops its "in" humor. Macabre humor in some instances. Outsiders have been shocked to hear the comments that fly in the operating room. "Crude," "insensitive," "brutal" are words I've heard.

But medical friends who have worked in this kind of pressure cooker know it as a way of relieving tension. A safety valve.

Many ~~pew-warmers~~ nonprofessionals would squirm if they heard some of the stories that fly round gatherings of ~~church people — priests, pastors and chaplains. But clergy work in a pressure cooker too. They need that release just as much as the medics. In fact,~~ professionals, but as long as people know what they are doing, as long as they know the time and place for such release, humor is a ~~very~~ healthy activity. Laughter is generally a far more useful response than anger. But sometimes we have to deliberately push ourselves to see the humor in a situation.

90 For clergy, weddings and funerals provide lots of grist for this kind of mill. Clergy are generally full of wild stories about crazy things that have happened during these transition times in people's lives. Years later, they tell those stories with relish.

But at the time, they found the events annoying and emotionally debilitating. If we compress time, to force ourselves to enjoy the humor as close as possible to the time of the annoying incident, we find a healthy outlet for anxiety.

95 When we meet small annoyances~

~~The problem with small problems is that~~ we tell ourselves, "Hey, I shouldn't get ~~my shirt~~ in a knot about this." ~~But of course we do. And since the incidents are not significant enough to discuss with a pastoral counselor, a colleague, or a spiritual director, we internalize them. But almost anyone enjoys sharing a laugh.~~ If we see the funny side, we can talk to anyone about ^{the} small problems) that otherwise can

100 ~~Small problems~~ accumulate ~~in the craw~~ and smolder away. ~~In at least some cases,~~ burnout results from an inability to deal with the little "pinches," that add up to ~~none of which in themselves are worth worrying about. Their totality, however, is~~ dynamite.

Laughing about a problem is not the same as avoiding it.) ~~People use many different means to avoid reality, including laughter. But~~ seeing the humor in a situation can mean

105 putting ~~getting~~ it into perspective ~~and refusing to be intimidated by it.~~ Repressed anger is debilitating: humor is invigorating. After a good laugh~ ~~If there's something to be done,~~ you ~~have more~~ energy left to do ~~its~~ something about the situation.

Notice, I'm talking about the small stuff. Laughter is an effective and healthy means of dealing with those things about which nothing much can be done and which will have

110 little impact on anybody in the long run. When it comes to industrial strength trauma, laughing would be avoidance at best and possibly even sick. So please don't conclude that laughter is appropriate for **all** problems.

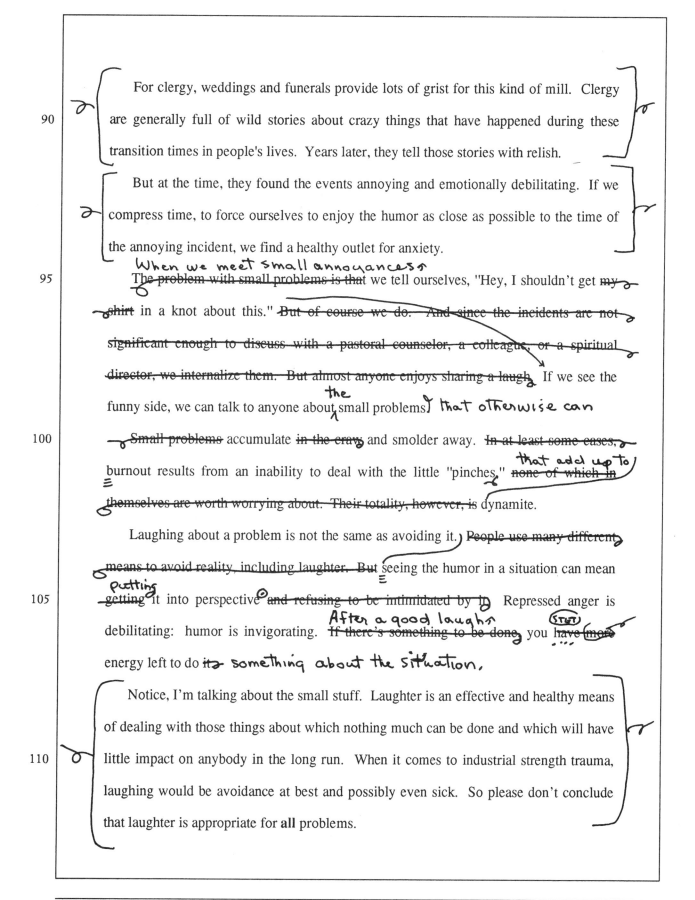

When humor is understood as an attitude, rather than as the ability to be funny, its uses are legion.

Group work

115 **head** ~~I hang out with various groupies~~ I am involved with a group of people who like to sit around in circles and have a "checking-in time" before they begin a meeting~~. This~~ which usually means we spend the first hour hearing how rotten everything has been for everybody. The theory is that once we get all this off our chests, we can focus on the issue at hand. Sometimes it means everybody starts the meeting depressed.

120 There are alternatives. I have been to meetings where we were invited to tell about something crazy or funny or bizarre or amusing that had happened to us recently. We smiled at some stories, laughed at others. It seemed to have the ~~same~~ intended effect of bringing us all into the group ~~so we could be "fully present.~~" And the resulting mood was far more positive.

125 **Humor and social justice**

Humor is ~~one of God's~~ a great gift to oppressed peoples. The oppressor can take away everything, but the ~~oppressor cannot take the soul.~~ mind And that ~~soul~~ mind can break forth in blazing anger and side-splitting laughter or be quietly refreshed by the quiet humor of those who have no strength left.

130 A classic example is the musical *Fiddler on the Roof*. In the final scene, the Jews are being kicked out of Russia by an oppressive Tsar. It is a deeply tragic scene.

One of the young men asks the rabbi, "We have been waiting so long for the Messiah. Wouldn't this be a good time for the Messiah to come?"

The rabbi reflects on how often his people have been kicked from one place to 135 another. "We'll just have to wait for the Messiah somewhere else," he says.

Tevya, the main character in the drama, had been wondering earlier why Jews keep their heads covered. "Ah!" he says. "Maybe that's why we always wear our hats."

Humor is also a life-saving and liberating device for individuals who are marginalized within their own society. One writer, Gary Boratto, ~~writing in a recent~~

140 ~~issue of *Rumors*,~~ reflects:

(run in) ~~I grew up in Toronto.~~ I was a small kid, weighing ~~80 pounds~~ 36.4 kg in grade ten.
Small people
~~Dealt that hand, you~~ make people laugh, get ~~your head~~ their heads kicked in, or run ~~like~~
and
~~heck.~~ I couldn't run very fast, valued my head, and so I learned a lot about

being funny on command.

145 ~~I'm sure this has been the case from the start of human history too.~~ Humor

is the defense of the weak, the only control of the powerless. As a matter of

fact, I can't really think of very many tall, ~~macho~~ funny people. But I can

name lots of short, weak ones who are funny."

Humor is a declaration of freedom. Humor is a fearful threat to dictators, single-

150 minded revolutionaries, bureaucrats, ~~television evangelists~~ and political correctness
their
fanatics. Humor helps us see ~~the~~ true colors ~~of the~~ "principalities and powers" even

though they themselves seldom do.

Humor and humanity

Humans are the only creatures with a sense of humor. Many animals can express joy

155 and exuberance, but no chimp ever got the point of a joke. No gorilla has ever groaned

in delight over a bad pun.

I like to think that since humor is unique to humans, and that since the biblical book of Genesis tells us that humans were created in the image of God, so our sense of humor is part of our divine image. Humor is God's holy gift to us all.

160 Look at the body language associated with anger or despair on one hand, and humor on the other. When we are angry, we drop our chins and hold our fists in front of our chests. When we are desperate or depressed or afraid, we clutch our own bodies and pull our necks into our shoulders. We fold ourselves toward the fetal position.

When we laugh, the head goes back, the arms fling out, and we are as totally

165 vulnerable as Christ made himself.

The ministry of laughter is incarnational, and very close to the ministry of the wounded healer. The one who laughs with us is also the one who cries with us. They are two sides of the same coin. Perhaps we cannot fully laugh until we have cried. And vice versa.

170 *Ralph Milton is publisher of Wood Lake Books and editor of* Rumors, *a magazine of Christian humor. He lives in Kelowna, B.C.*

Local History

A regional historical association hires you to edit a 32-page local history. The potential readership is large because tentative arrangements exist for the provincial ministry of tourism to post the document on its Web site and to produce it as a booklet to be distributed free through resorts and tourist information booths. The manuscript is rambling and not written very well. Five or six scattered paragraphs are, however, sharp and to the point. As you check the spelling of a name in *The Canadian Encyclopedia,* you realize that at least one of those paragraphs has been copied from it almost word for word. What do you do? Consider various potential reactions.

Starting Out and Thriving as a Freelancer

An instructor is turning her course notes into a book for people who are interested in freelancing but who cannot attend her classes. She has written the following table of contents.

She asks you, as an editor and one of her more successful former students, to help her. The two of you agree you can best serve her by analyzing the structure of the proposed book as revealed by the outline, making suggestions based on that analysis, and doing some editing on the table of contents itself to bring it closer to an acceptable final form. (She wouldn't presume on your time to the extent of asking you to look at the whole manuscript.)

CONTENTS

Chapter 1 Introduction: Do you have what it takes?

What do you know?

What this book will do for you

What this book won't do for you

Chapter 2 Getting work

When you have no experience

Do you have what it takes to be your own boss?

Are you capable?

When to give up

How to get experience

When you have some experience

The key to getting work — networking

Warming up the cold call

Your résumé

The covering letter

Following up that first contact

When you've got the job

Invoicing and accounting

Chapter 3 Startup costs

Should one begin part-time or jump right in?

Should you register your business?

Childhood Inoculations

A family physician brings the following manuscript to you to desktop. "Before you produce it," he says, "would you see if there's any way I can get the message across more effectively? Parents seem really confused about the needles I give their children. If I could give them something they'd actually read and remember, I could save myself a lot of time."

Note: Needless to say, this information is not to be taken as the latest word in pediatric advice. It's actually somewhat out of date.

Inoculations -- often called needles or shots -- are one of 20th-century medicine's great gifts. Twice my own grandmother held her baby daughters as they died of diphtheria, and a few years later she regarded my father's surviving the same disease as a miracle. As recently as your own childhood, diseases such as German measles (rubella) and mumps were seen as just another part of growing up, even though complications left hundreds of children maimed for life.

Today, a few inoculations can protect your child from a host of diseases. But the needles have to be given!

Please let me follow the current recommendations of the Canadian Paediatric Society in immunizing your child.

The first needle I will give your child is called the DPT vaccine. It protects against diphtheria, whooping cough (the fancy name is pertussis), and tetanus. The vaccine has to be given in four doses, with a booster a little later. I give the first dose at age two months.

There's a good chance your baby may have no reaction whatsoever. Or, within a few hours, she may become fussy with a slight fever and a reddish sore spot at the point of injection in her arm or thigh. This reaction shouldn't last more than two days -- call me if it does or if the fever goes high. In most cases, you can just cuddle her a bit extra, give her a cool bath, and use children's acetaminophen every four hours.

25   I give the other primary doses of DPT vaccine at ages 4, 6, and 18 months. There's a slightly increased chance of a low-grade reaction with each dose. Again, use acetaminophen and call me if the fever is high or if it lasts more than 48 hours.

30   Unfortunately, the media have given a lot of publicity to a handful of cases in which a severe reaction to the pertussis vaccine led to a child's becoming brain damaged. As a result, some parents decide not to risk that needle for their child. That's foolish. Tragedies happen, but the risk is so small that it's statistically insignificant. But whooping cough can be a nasty -- even fatal --
35   disease, especially for a young child.

      Between ages 4 and 6, your child should have a booster DPT shot. A tetanus-only booster is then required every 10 years for life.

      Also during your child's 2-month checkup, I will give an oral
40   polio vaccine. It must be repeated at 4 and 18 months, and a booster is needed between ages 4 and 6.

      Reactions to the polio vaccine are rare (and it's in a sweet syrup, not a needle!). But call me if your baby develops diarrhoea or signs of a tummy ache.

45   The third vaccine I will give your baby at 2 months is fairly new, but it's a godsend. It's called the HIB vaccine (hemophilus influenza type B bacteria) and it protects against meningitis. Bacterial meningitis is not a common disease, but it kills in as

50 many as 5 percent of cases and causes brain damage in many
more. Until recently, the irony was that the illness is most common
in children under 24 months but no vaccine could be used until 18
months. Now we have one that can be used at 2 months; followup
doses are given at 4 and 6 months and between 12 and 18 months.
<u>Please</u> let me give it to your child. There's rarely any side effect
55 beyond a low-grade fever and some soreness at the point of
injection.

The final vaccine your baby needs gives protection against
measles, mumps, and rubella (German measles), so it's often called
MMR. There are occasional slight reactions -- a low fever and
60 maybe a rash -- about a week after the needle, which is given at 12
months. Call me if your baby seems really sick. Also, talk to me
first if your baby has been showing any signs of allergy to eggs.
The vaccine is made with eggs, so we don't give it to highly allergic
children.

65 Remember, these vaccines protect your baby, but I can give
them only if you let me!

Copy Editing

Copy editing, says *The Chicago Manual of Style*, is an editor's "most time-consuming task. It requires close attention to every detail in a manuscript, a thorough knowledge of what to look for and of the style to be followed, and the ability to make quick, logical, and defensible decisions."

It also requires at least tacit agreement between editor and employer about what copy editing comprises, in general and in particular. The Standard Freelance Editorial Agreement specifies "editing for grammar, spelling, punctuation, and other mechanics of style; checking for consistency of mechanics and for internal consistency of facts; inserting of head levels and approximate placement of art; editing tables, figures, and lists; notifying designer of any unusual production requirements."

Can any more be expected? Frequently, yes. Although stylistic editing, general fact checking, detailed markup or coding, and proofreading are separate editorial tasks, it is often the copy editor who ends up doing them.

What the copy editor does depends on the particular manuscript and on the situation. The type of publication, the time and money available for editing, the author's availability to answer queries and willingness to accept changes, and the production process to be used all inform the editor's job. Thus, the situation, as set out in the introduction for each of these exercises, is an integral part of the self-test.

Banana Peels

An author of romance fiction has been saved from embarrassment by generations of vigilant copy editors. With sublime faith in them, she has long since given up worrying about details, spelling, and punctuation. But she doesn't like being bugged by editors. "Just do whatever you think best," she tells them.

The publisher puts up with this author because her books sell well—thanks in part to all those devoted editors.

Today, you are the copy editor, faced with the opening chapters of two different books. "You can't make them into great fiction," says the managing editor, "but try to ensure they make some sense and are consistent. In addition to copy editing, rescue the worst of her overwriting and clumsy phrasing. If you find places that may need more editing or run into points that you can't check, query me in the margin."

The house style follows *The Chicago Manual of Style,* with *The Canadian Oxford Dictionary* used for spelling.

Phyllis

A river rushed along the sidewalk--its centre flowed
quickly and deeply confused, and hesitating eddies
swirled along its edges. It spilled in a frothing gush
into the intersection, freed from the constricting
buildings and lines of traffic that contained them.
The stream of Xmas shoppers parted for barely an
instant to serge around a still figure, a slender
impediment to their giddy and single-minded pursuits.
And then, in an instant, she was gone.

A rushing roar. Cold damp. Faint smell of salt. Where
was she? With a sudden happy lurch of her heart, she
knew she was at home, by the sea, safe and protected.
The sharp smell of exhaust fumes, the roar of the
traffic -- these were the reality. This wasn't Cape
Bretton Island; it was hated Toronto on a cold gray
day, and she was lying on the sidewalk with such a

20 stabbing in her left ankle that she wanted only to

faint again from the pain, and the embarrassment.

"We've got an ambulance on the way, Miss, just

stay there a bit longer. You really should have a

check up." Phyllis struggled to sit up, but a firm

25 hand resisted her attempt. She looked up into the grey

eyes of the door man that was gathering her scattered

belongings--worn out purse, scuffed paper back, crisp

Holt, Renfrew bag--and tears sprung to her eyes. His

clear, blue, eyes and the peppery smell of his after

30 shave ... Grandfather? No of course not, Grandfather

was . . . where? Tears filled her eyes.

The wale of the siren brought her once again to

the dreary present. Several passerby had stopped to

help; kind hands wisked her into the ambulance and

35 soon she sank back on the pillow of the stretcher

thing (what are they called?).

"I'm Nurse Czirfuz." The voice was unpleasantly high-

pitched. Reading from the report, the nurse furrowed

40 her brow. "It says you ~~accidently~~ slipped on the

sidewalk. Let's have a look at that ankel before the

dr. comes along. We've seen alot of accidents to-

night," she added unkindly as if Phyllis should have

been more considerate. In Phyllis' view, the waiting

45 room had had less people than it usually did. In fact,

it had seemed as quite as a cemetary.

In an attempt to stop the tears that were

threatening, Phyllis concentrated on the nurse's name

tag—Joanne Csirfusz, as she offered her sore right

50 ankle.

"I'm sure I'm alright." Phyllis muttered in a

vane effort to control the shakeing of her voice.

"Ah, the beautiful nurse Jo-anne! What's the

problem here." A handsome man wisked into the cubical

55 as the nurse turned an unbecoming shade of pink and

simpered in welcome. Hopefully, this was the doctor.

As he Carefully holding her ankle in his strong hand,

she explained about her accident.

Ed: whisk the right word here?

"We've had a few people in here this week who've fallen on the ice, but very few of them have been badly injured, I think half the reason is that people simply don't look where their going. You're leg will be sore for a few days, but I can't forsee any lasting affects." Phyllis recieved the news that there were no permenant damage to her leg with relief.

Suddenly, the doctor picked up the paper book Phyllis had put down when the obnoxous nurse had arrived. "Is this your's?" he asked in amazment as he looked at the title; Principals of Editing and Reccommendations for Applying Them.

"I've been looking every where for a copy of this!" he expostulated. "Where did you get it!"

Wanda

I looked around the room with satisfaction. Everything
was ready for my visitor. The cushions on the sofas
were plump and inviting; the brightly-burning fire was
beginning to warm the room; the forsythia on the
mantle glowed; the grande piano (how the movers had
struggled to get that to the third floor!) seemed
almost alive. I felt as if I could see it breathe. In
spite of my pleasure with the scene, I felt oddly
nervous.

Five years ago, it hadn't taken much to persuade
us to buy the house--the view from the banks of the
Ottawa River was spectacular, the house was desirable,
we had wanted to live in the capitol city--everything
was perfect. And the price the sellers were asking
seemed more than reasonable for a 19th-century gem
that had belonged to a prominent politician. We had
done minor renovations and spent a lot of time
decorating each room--why did it feel that it still
didn't belong to us?

(margin note) Ed: Can you feel as if something's breathing?

(line numbers in left margin: 5, 10, 15, 20)

Below I saw my guest coming up the walk; he disappeared into the porch ~~where he removed his hat~~ and ~~before~~ he rang the bell. It was too late for me to change my mind.

Sam Wellesley was younger than I had expected and a bit nervous. He obviously knew who I was--a pleasant surprise--so I chattered on about the recital I was to give at the National Arts Center, the next week.

"I've been having some trouble with my vocal chords recently. I've been visiting a specialist and hopefully my voice will be in good shape." I paused to pass him the cup of Earle Gray tea. "The doctor reccommended I drink herbal tea twice a day, but oh! how I miss my cup of Asam!" I knew I was beginning to put on my prima donna act. I hated it. It always bubbled to the surface when I was feeling pressurized. I fought to bring my voice under control. I might as well get right to the point about why I had asked him to come.

Ed: Suggest "stressed, under pressure?"

"Sam—I may call you Sam?—" I wasn't doing this
well. "When my husband and I bought this house, we
wanted to recreate it as it must of been in the eight-
eenth-century. We felt our roll was that of custodians
of an historical treasure, and had great fun
researching what it must have been like and how we
could replicate that and still make it a house with
the comforts of the 21st century. The house has many
idiosyncragies, but we've learned to live with it." I
paused. "When we came to this, the third floor, it was
just an attic, full of dust and mice mainly, but we
found some papers....old diaries...stuff like that." I
shifted uncomfortably and got up to light the fire.
Outside, the leaves were falling from the trees and
the room was filled with a bright, lemony light.

"I'll let you read them if you decide you want
to help us. In one of them it said, "Do not argue with
this house or it will retaliate.""

Canadian Railways

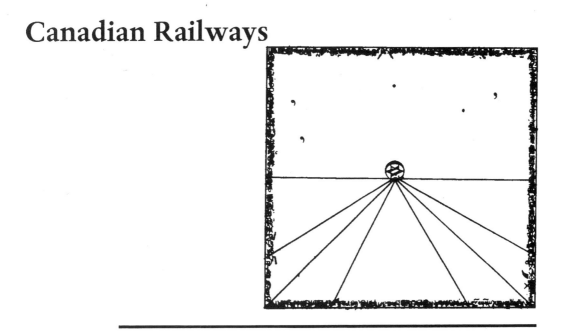

You're applying for a job. The chief copy editor hands you some sample manuscript, telling you it is from a popular work of short pieces on Canada. It has been through a structural edit and a reading level check, and the author swears the facts, including the names of the railways, are correct.

You are asked to copy edit, creating a style that can be used for the rest of the work. If you suspect errors of fact, correct those you can check quickly and query the others. Assume the author will see the edited manuscript but doesn't have the time or patience to put up with many queries.

CANADIAN RAILWAYS

Railways have a special place in Canadian

history. During the nineteenth Century, the

country was shaped as much by 'terriers'

5   (rail construction laborours) as by

ploughmen.

        Horse powered railcars were used very

early at mines and quarries -- probably

including the fort of Louisberg in the 18th

10   century -- and a steam-driven winch pulled

cable cars up a hill to the site of the

Citadel in Quebec City. But the first true

railroad in Canada was the Champlain and

Saint Lawrence Railroad, opened 21 July 1836

15   between Montréal (actually, Laprairie) and

lac Champlain (actually, St-Johns, on the

Richelieu River.) The first railroad in the

Maritimes, only nine and one-half kilometers

long, opened September 19, 1839, a mere 5

20   years later.

Longer lines were soon built, espeically

after the Legislature of the United Canadas

25

30

passed the <u>Guarantee Act</u>, in 1849 putting a 6

percent ceiling on the interest rate for half

of the bonds used to finance a railway more

than seventy-five miles in length. The St.

Laurence and Atlantic (between Montreal and

Portland, ME) and the Great Western (from

Niagara Falls toWindsor, Ontario, completed

in January, 1854) were privately owned but

emjoyed various kinds of government support

and expenditure. So did the Grand Trunk

railway, which ran from Sarnia to Montréal

and was completed in 1860.

35   These and other lines in teh early

provinces tyed together manufacturing centres

and hinterlands. The growing network played

an essential role in Canadian

industrialisation: opening new markets,

40   vastly increasing the demand for iron, steel,

and fuel (first wood and then coal) and for

labour, and even creating railway towns--

centers that existed primarily to build and

service equipment and to provide for

45   travelers' needs. Without formal plans,

cities themselves came to be centered not on

manufacturing or trading establishments but

on their railway stations, loading docks, and

yards.

50   The possibilities of railroads also gave

British nationalists a boost. Many of the

colonies natural trade routes are water ways,

running north-south and terminating in US

cities. With the railways, trade could be

55   chaneled east/west, keeping it above the

forty-fifth parallel in the west.

The railroads of the first half of the

19th century were, however, fairly short-run.

Visionaries dreamt of extending the iron

60   roads "from sea to shining sea." Skeptics

suggested that the rail concept, created in

England--a small country with a mild climate

--would be paralyzed by the distances,

climatic rigors, and rugged terrain of the

65   northern Colonies.

    What they were forgetting was the

onslaught of technological innovation, home-

grown and from over-seas, that was gradually

overcoming a variety of challenges. Vastly

70   improved engineering made possible the

construction of previously-impossible tunnels

and bridges. The development of the rotary

snowplow (by Mr. J. W. Elliott, later

improved by O. Jull) enabled more dependable

75   travel which until then was often paralysed

in the winter. Time zones--conceived by Sir.

Standford Fleming, one of the dominion's

great rail road engineers--overcame confusion

in scheduling.

80   Not surprisingly, the dreamers and

entrepreneurs won, although not without

heated quarrelling. The risk, and sometimes

the loss, of vast sums of money, and several

political scandals. A condition of the

85 British North American Act was the completion

of the Intercolonial Railway, a line linking

the Maritimes and the Province of Canada. By

1876, it ran from Halifax to Ste-Flavie,

Quebec, covering some 1100 km; within a few

90 more years, merger with the Grand Trunk

Railway brought it to Point Levis, Que., and

eventually to Montréal. And as is well-known,

the promise of a true intercontinental link--

95 | a mari usque ad mare -- was a key in

persuading B.C. to enter confederation in

1871.

Highway Horror

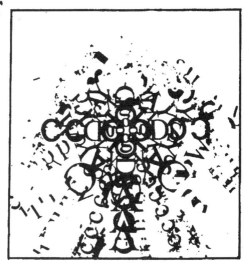

You work for the publisher of a regional supplement that is inserted each week into a large metropolitan newspaper that uses Canadian Press style.

This week, winter finally hit the area. From a variety of sources, a junior reporter has pulled together the following overview of the storm's effects. Now you have to edit it. And the production desk needs your copy—quickly.

By Jan South

Many Toronto residents found themselves on skid
row early Monday when a snow storm hit an area
largely limited to south-Central Ontario,
particularly around the Lake.

Beginning near 7 am in the morning, as the
temperature dropped to an overnight low of -7
degrees celsius city streets and highways were
turned to ice by a major precipitation of
freezing rain.

Hitting just as the morning traffic rush
began, amny cars and even some busses went
skidding and spinning along roads turned to ice
by the storm, particularly in hilly areas of
thecity.

The traffic problems caused by the
unexepected morning storm was repeated later in
the day on Monday just after 7.30 p.m. when a
ligth light snowfall began. Coating streets and
causing numerous accidents. By the time the
weather system had passed, it had dumped almost
4 inches of snow on the city. For a second time
cars traveling up hills in the city core were
again stalled.

25 There was also ground-level blizzard
conditions with white outs and winds to 75 km an
hour north of the city in York Region. Police
officials there said that during the monring
storm fifty-two accidents were reported. The OPP
30 also reported a large number, and all three law
units said there were likely many more that were
not reported.

It caught road maintenence crews unaware,
bu t the cleanup deparment said crews were sent
35 out as soon as they reported to work.Ray
Johnson, Toronto highways adminsitrator said the
storm, "kicked us right in the pants. I don't
want to see another one of these". He said he
immediately diverted crew members coming on to
40 the job to cleaning and sanding streets

Harold Russel, Environment Canada
meteorologist said "Freezing rain turning to
snow coupled with extreme precipatation in
during a short period sometimes occur under
45 thunderhead sitiuations. Hopefully it won't
happen again quite that way this winter.'

50   Almost all the rest of the province was
clear and dry. An equally viscous snow squal hit
the Niagra Peninsula, turning streets and
highways around St. Catherine's to glass, and
backing up traffic on the Queen E. Way for
several hours..

30

Desktop Scanners

You are a copy editor and proofreader in the marketing department of a large corporation. One day an assistant in the Information Services Department (ISD) asks you if you have time to proofread a report he has been working on. It will be distributed to every member of ISD, so he doesn't want embarrassing errors.

You say you don't know much about the technology ISD works with. He responds that it doesn't matter, since all his information on technology is correct. His problem is that he's not much good at spelling; besides, he has worked on this piece so long he probably couldn't spot an obvious error. "Please don't tell me there's no photo of the HP Scanjet," he concludes. "I just couldn't find one."

A quick glance tells you the piece needs copy editing. You ask your friend to come back in an hour, ready to answer questions. Then you check with the chief secretary of Information Services, who keeps a style sheet. From it you verify that the following terms are styled correctly:

binary	HP	PostScript
DEST	Macintosh	Scanjet
dithered	MS-DOS	sheet-fed
dpi	OCR	Tagged-Image File Format
flatbed	PC Scan	

Now go back to your office and clean up your friend's report. Keep a list of questions to ask when he returns.

FEATURES OF TWO POPULAR DESKTOP SCANNERS:

HP Scanjet
• OCR capability available
• scans half-tones
• can reproduce 16 shades of gray
• resolution: 300 dpi
• flatbed
• approximate price: $2,700.

DEST PC Scan 1000
• no OCR capability
• scans half-tones
• can reproduce 16 shades of gray
• resolution: 300 dpi
• sheet-fed
• approximate price: $4,000.

Neither the HP Scanjet nor the DEST is currently supported by ISD.

WHAT SHOULD I CONSIDER IN CHOOSING A SCANNER?

Among the important features to consider in choosing a scanner are:

Sheet-fed, Flatbed or Hand-held:

A *sheet-fed* scanner can scan only from unbound sheets of paper, as might fit in a typewriter carriage. It cannot scan a page bound in a magazine or book. There are necessary limits too on the size of the original, paper thickness and paper finish. The principle advantage is the ability of some sheet fed machines to feed through a series of pages automatically.

A *flatbed* scanner can scan from bound pages, of any finish orthickness. A wider range of sizes can usually be accomodated, and autofeeders are avaliable for some models. Flatbed scanners are more expensive then sheet-fed models.

Hand-held scanners can scan originals of any size, but the process can be laborious. They are most affective for reading in short passages of text or figures. They are not practical for scanning images or any large amounts of material.

Text or Image Scanning

All scanners can scan both text and images. Some scan images only, some only text. Text-only scanners are commonly referred to as optical character readers.

Storage format:

The method of storage used for scanned images must be compatible with the applications used. Emerging standards are:

EPS - Tagged-Image File Format; offers easy transportability between Macintosh and MS-DOS environments.

TIFF - Encapsulated PostScript; the most effective format for use with PostScript printers.

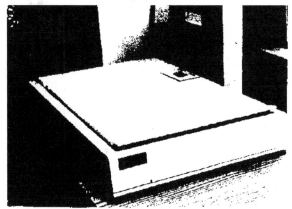

A dithered phtograph of the DEST PC Scan 1020. Grays are simulated by different dot densities.

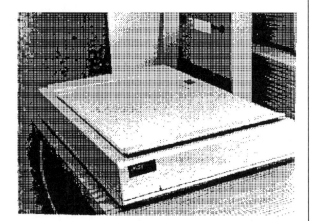

Abinary scan of the same photograph, again showing a DEST Scan 1020. Each scanned sample is designated either black or white.

The Southgate Approach

You have just taken over as the volunteer editor of a monthly community newsletter, *The Southgate Approach*. The previous editor had developed a style sheet to enable her to impose some consistency on submissions.

The present style sheet is a little difficult to follow and somewhat idiosyncratic. You hope to revise it some day. But for the time being, you have to apply it to the spectacular diversity of writers supplying you with copy.

Style Hints: *The Southgate Approach*

SPELLING

Generally American, using *Webster's New Collegiate Dictionary.* Note the following patterns.

labor	enroll(ment)
neighbor	fulfill(ment)
honor(able)	traveling
favor(ite)	labeled
glamour (**but** glamorous)	focusing
	buses and busing
judgment	goodbye
acknowledgment	
	percent (1 word)
center (and centered)	cigarette
theater	pajamas
meter (as in parking meter)	ax
	mold
organize	marijuana
notarize	
analyze	

practice (n and v)
licence (n and v)

Use the following exceptions to *Webster's.*

cheque (as in pay cheque)
catalogue
metre and kilometre

Hyphenate prefixes only to avoid confusion. Do not worry about doubling a vowel. (Do not depend on *Webster's* for hyphenation.)

preregistration	***but***
understaffed	re-create (to make again)
semiactive	re-cover (cover again)
coauthor	non-English-speaking
cooperate	self-reliant
reenrollment	

Watch out for proper nouns. Many local organizations use British spelling.

Junior Y Daycare Centre
Harbourfront

Close up suffixes and compound words, except when confusion may result.

chequebook	vice-president
headache	attorney-general
highrise	one-third
townhouse	two-year-olds
buildup (n)	two- and three-year-olds
build up (verb)	

TIMES AND DATES

The format for specific dates is day, month, date, year; use abbreviations and omit year unless needed for clarity. Do not abbreviate approximate dates.

Wed., Apr. 26,
on Dec. 7, 1972
but in April 1972 (no comma when no day given)
on Wednesdays in December

Use a.m. and p.m. for times (close up, but do not omit periods). Do not substitute a hyphen for the word "to". Use "noon" and "midnight" rather than 12:00. Separate hours and minutes with a colon.

2:30 p.m.
noon
12:30 p.m.
8:00 a.m. to 9:45 a.m. (note colon with zeros for even hours)

PUNCTUATION

Use the great Canadian compromise: double quotation marks for quoted words, with single quotation marks inside (American style); put other punctuation marks inside or outside according to context (English style).

"The board," said Mr. Williams, "should investigate."
Mr. Williams said that the board "should investigate".
The president announced, "We will open by singing 'O Canada'."

Use the serial comma.

children, young adults, and seniors
The board will decide whether to keep the rule, change it, or put the matter to the residents.

NUMBERS

Spell out one through ten, rounded amounts, and a number that begins a sentence.

seven million (but $7 million, to avoid spelling out "dollars")
about one hundred people
Twenty-seven candidates filed papers.

But be consistent within any group of numbers.

and 47 voted in favor; 3 abstained.
three- to eleven-year-olds *or* 3- to 11-year-olds

The following always take Arabic numerals:
- money amounts ($4, $7.95, 85 cents)
- percentages (47 percent; in tables only, 63%)
- school classes (Grade 6)
- time and date (see below for details)

Ordinals follow the same rules as above, but note that ordinals are often not needed in dates, addresses, etc.

tenth
21st   ***but*** May 21

For money amounts of $1 and more, always use Arabic numerals and a dollar symbol (rewrite as necessary to avoid beginning of sentence).

For money amounts of less than $1, avoid the cents symbol (which is ugly in the text typeface).

$0.75 *or* 75 cents

If a passage gives only even dollar amounts, omit the decimal zeros. But use them consistently if amounts are mixed.

$5, $10, and $15
but $5.00, $10.75, and $15.00

ADDRESSES

1745 Finch Ave. West (spell out West or East; single letter abbreviations get lost)
470 Stafford Rd., Suite 1405,

Apply the same general rules for first and subsequent uses of place names as for personal names.

The traffic congestion on Finch Avenue
The noise from Keele Street continued
The Keele/Finch corner

Omit province (and city/neighbourhood if clear in context) from addresses that readers might go to personally; include city, province (traditional abbreviations), and postal code when readers are expected to use the mail.

Pick up a brochure from the Harold Ballard Aquatic Centre, 5100 Yonge St.
Send the application to the Southgate Board of Governors, 25 Southgate Mall Dr., New Mimico, Ont. M9N 4Q6.

NAMES AND TITLES

First use: always use first and last name. Add title only if helpful or if required by courtesy or custom.

Barbara Baker   or Vice-president Barbara Baker
Y. C. Yeske   or Dr. Y. C. Yeske
(note space between initials)
but not Mr. James Smith, or Ms. Alyson Hoodwink

Subsequent uses: same title plus last name. Use Ms. (not Miss or Mrs.) for all women.

Mr. Smith
Dr. Yeske
Vice-president Baker
Ms. Hoodwink (note period for Ms.)

Organization names: full name, upper and lower case, on first use in any article. Short form may be used for subsequent references, generally lowercased.

Southgate Property Management (Southgate)
Toronto Board of Education (T.B.E., the board, the education board)
Junior Y Daycare Centre (the Daycare Centre, the Centre)
Sunnystreet Public School (Sunnystreet, the school)
the Budget Committee (the committee)
but the ad-hoc parking committee (all lowercase because it's not an officially named committee)

Titles and positions: capitalize generic titles if they precede the name, lower case if they follow the name or stand alone.

Councillor Bruce Richer   Bruce Richer, councillor for York East

Sergeant Julie McComber   Julie McComber, a sergeant

When in doubt if you have a true title or merely a job description (superintendent, librarian, teacher), go lower case. In exceedingly long titles, go lower case anyway.

Department of Highways administrative assistant Hector Rzpecki public relations subcommittee acting honorary chairperson Gyan Singh

INCLUSIVE LANGUAGE

Unless an organization specifically requires traditional terminology, use non-sexist words.

chairperson   not chairman
staff time   not man hours
letter carrier   not mailman

ABBREVIATIONS

All abbreviations, including acronyms, take periods.

Rd.
S.G.R.C.
R.C.M.P.
Mr.
U.S.

GENERAL TIPS ON EDITING AND MARKUP

Boldface the following:
- bylines (always flush left, under head; at least two line spaces above byline and one below; always set up with lowercase "by")
- subheads (line space above, no periods at end)
- in letters, "Dear Editor" openings (set flush left, no space below), and signatures (set flush right)

Italicize the following:
- *The Southgate Approach, The Approach, Approach* reporters
- any editorial comment at the top or bottom of a story; separate from text with a line space
- second-level subheads (e.g., those used for listing events in the Conservation Authority or Library columns. Run into line, precede with standard paragraph indent, and follow with period.)

Bullets take standard paragraph indents.

Every paragraph takes an indent. When copy has been typed block-style (spaces between paragraphs, no indents), delete the spaces and mark for indent.

NEVER USE FULL CAPS FOR EMPHASIS.

All headlines have a verb, real or implied, preferably in present tense. (Regular columns have titles, not headlines, hence no verb necessary.)

Watch out for hidden advertising, especially in columns by merchants. Avoid it if possible. If not, balance references to specific products, prices, or services by equally favorable mention of a competitor.

There is no need to mark up sizes, faces, etc., for normal headlines, body text, etc., as the typesetter keeps all standard specs on file.

The standard columns—We Get Letters, Goings on at Southgate Library, At the Conservation Areas, From Hair On, From the Dentist's Chair, Rec Center Happenings, and the school reports—have standing heads. Don't spend time or money getting them reset.

Material for the January issue of the Aproach

From Irene Smith

GOINGS ON AT SOUTHGATE LIBRARY

5   The South Gate Library, at 1785 Finch Ave. W., North York, has a full slate of programmes planned for the coming months.

      Children may chose from activities ranging from origami to a Winter Reading Club. Young adults will also find activities geared to their interests.

10

      All activities are free. Please note the pre-registration is required for some programmes. More information is available from the library staff by phoning (416) 630-9585.

15

Children

      Teddybear Travels Reading Club. This weekly reading get-together is for the two to threes. Please pre-register. A parent or other adult must accompany each child. Will start Jan. 4th, 1992, 11:00 - 11:45.

20

      Operation S.E.A.R.C.H. School-age children can enrol in the Seek Early Achievement Reading Club Heats. As specail agents, they will TRAVEL to far-off worlds, stop an inter-galactic villan and SOLVE a planetary mystery. Begins Monday, Jan. 4th. Every Monday from 3:30 to 4:30.

25

Olympia Games: Relay games, races, etc. especially for the seven to twelve year olds. Tuesday, January 19, 2.00-3:00.

Origimi Is Easy. An artist will demonstrate how to make figurines and jewellery from folded paper. Ages 8 to 12. Thursday, Jan. 28, 3.30-4:30.

Go Hog Wild: Some of the activities are pig mask craft and "pig" racing. Ages 7 to 12. Tuesday February 2, 3:30-5.

Cartooning for Kids. This cleaver drawing program is aimed for the eight to twelves. Please pre-register. Every Friday from January 9 to February 5. 4:00 to 5:00.

Young Adults

Cycling safely. A representative of the Ont. Cycling Association will provide tips on winter bicycling and maintenance in this 3 part series. For young peoel in Grade 7 and up. Please pre-register. Thursdays, January 14-28, 7-8 pm.

Chinese Food for You. Young people in Grade 7-13 can learn how to make simple, nutricious Chinese meals. Please pre-register. Saturday, Jan 30, 2-4 pm

column for The Approach from Amadeo Rossini

From Hair On

Amadeo Rossini
(Mr. Rossini is a hair- and skin-care consultant for a local beauty salon. He also works part time for a major cosmetics company)

"NEW YEAR, NEW YOU"

The new year is upon us, and what better way to celebrate this than with a terrific new hairstyle, and a revamped skincare/makeup programme. Not only will your fabulous new look add glamour to your looks. It will also help to eliminate those 'mid-winter blues" that we all experience after the holidays.

Start with a fabulous new hairstyle by having a consultation with a trusted hair stylist. If you haven't yet found 'your perfect hairdresser", ask those friends of yours, whose hair styles you admir, who their hairstylist is. The trned for hairstyles this year is towards shorter looks. What makes this years' hairstyles different than those of the past. are 2 things: Firstly, all of the new, shorter loods, are accentuated and made more exciting by the use of mousses, styling gels and styling glazes. (Ask your hair stylist for reccomendation of styling products to suit your needs)

Secondly, today's proffesional salon haircolouring methods give all hair styles a shine, a texture and a nuance never before achieved. If your personality is one of enjoying to be noticed, there are many hair-styling options open to you to make you turn heads. However if you prefer to have fashionable-looking hair (but not in a radical way) , then there are also many haircolouring options opened for you.

For the latter woman who would like to try a subtle change in her image for the new year, and who has never had her ahir coloured beofre, I would suggest a fabulous new salon technique called "glossing." "Glossing" gives you a taste, and a preview of all the terrific benefits that todays hair colouring gives—shine, texture, and a look of vigour. Clossing only takes about fifteen minutes in the salon and requires absolutely no maintenance.

Hair colour these days   is a form of make up for your ahir. Having just a good haircut, or a good hair style, may be nice. But for a totaly fashion-right, up to the minute look, colour your ahir and colour your life this year.

Next month we will discuss some changes in skincare and make-up for today's woman.
from Amadeo Rossini, Southgate Beauty Salon

Let's Go Skiing at the Conservation
Areas

Stick your cross-country skis in the
car and take a short drive to winter
fun. Whether you're a novice or a
skilful skier, the conservation areas
north of the city offer a variety of
trails.

Albion Hills Conservation Area, 10
kilometres north of Bolton on Highway
50, offers beginner, intermediate and
expert trails. There are ski rentals and
a heated chalet.

Palgrave Forest and Wildlife Area,
two kilometres north of Albion Hills on
Highway 50, has intermediate and expert
trails.

Bruce's Mill Conservation Area, on
Stouffville Road three kilometres east
of Highway 404, boasts beginner and
intermediate trails. There is also
outdoor skating. A heated chalet and ski
rentals are available on weekends.

25   Albion Hills and Bruce's Mill are
        open daily, if weather conditions allow,
        from 9:30 a.m. to 4:30 p.m. Palgrave is
        open weekends only. The trails at all
        three are track set.

30   Trail fees are $6 for adults, $2.50
        for children, and $15 for a family.
        Children under age five are admitted
        free.

        The grounds of the Kortright Centre
35   for Conservation, three kilometres west
        of Highway 400 on Pine Valley Drive,
        have marked but ungroomed trails at the
        beginner and intermediate levels. They
        are open 10 a.m. to 4 p.m. daily.
40   Admission fees are $4 for adults and
        $2.25 for children and seniors.

        For up-to-date information on trail
        conditions and on other winter
        activities, call the Toronto Region
45   Conservation Authority at 416-661-6600. A
        free winter information package,
        including cross-country ski trail maps,
        is available.

Reunion at Coyote Lodge

Your cousin is planning a reunion of fly-fishing enthusiasts from across the province and from the adjacent border states. She asks you to have a look at the directions she has roughed out. She plans to draw the final map with drafting pens, type the copy to fit next to it, and then photocopy the whole piece.

2

4

6

To Get To "Coyote Lodge" . . .

Follow Highway 53 north to the Delhi Road. Turn right
and follow the road for about 1 kilometre to the T
junction. Take the right-hand (gravel) road along the
south shore of Loon Lake to "Coyote Lodge." It has
ample parking for cars and RV's.

8

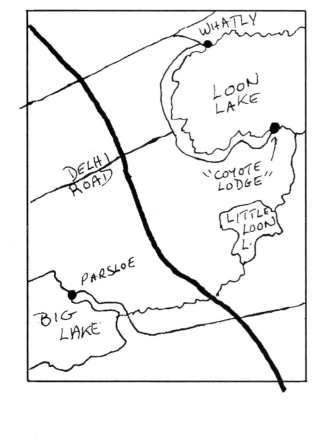

The Women's Matrix

As a freelancer who works primarily for nontraditional publishers, you have had some interesting clients but rarely one as harassed as Audrey Arbuthnot, the head of a small, impecunious social agency. Trying to find out what she wants you to do was difficult ("the report just has to be better" was her refrain). During your one meeting with her, you did manage to settle the details of your agreement (see the next page), but she was constantly interrupted by phone calls and staff queries. You suspect that you should prepare carefully for any further encounters if your time is not to be eaten up.

This exercise comes from a bygone era: the age of North York and the much-lamented Etobicoke in Toronto, the age of the Meech Lake Accord and of a federal agency called "Manpower Canada". Metropolitan Toronto and its constituent cities are no more, and federal agencies have continued their cycle of death and rebirth under new names. But notice that one detail is as fresh as the day it was written—an underfunded social services agency.

The Women's Matrix

Memo to: Copy editor
From: Director, Women's Matrix

Attached please find five of the reports to be included in the annual report of The Women's Matrix. The remainder, including the auditor's report, will follow within the week.

As discussed, please create and apply a consistency of style to the full range of reports to be included in the final report. Any tightening and shortening that you can do to reduce printing and mailing costs would be appreciated.

If you have any questions about the material in these reports, please contact me and I will try to resolve them for you. I would request that you do not discuss queries with individual reporters or officials, as our organization is chronically understaffed and overworked.

The fee you quoted is acceptable to us. Because our organization is chronically underfunded, the amount cannot be raised even if the work takes more time than anticipated. So, I request that you proceed as expeditiously as possible. That is a further reason for directing inquiries only to me.

Upon completion of your editing, the manuscript for the report will be forwarded directly to Alyson Entwhistle, a recent high school graduate who has offered to word process the document for us. She will deliver the completed pages to our usual printer.

The report will be distributed to all of our members and supporters immediately. During the coming year, it will also be used for the purposes of recruiting volunteers and for fund-raising purposes.

Thank you for your willingness to undertake this task.

Audrey J. Arbuthnot

AN OUTREACH ARM OF THE HOSPITAL OF SAINT FELICITAS, THE WOMEN'S MATRIX SEEKS TO PROVIDE OPPORTUNITIES FOR IMMIGRANT AND REFUGEE WOMEN THROUGH NETWORKING AND SOCIAL SUPPORT. TAX RECEIPTS WILL BE ISSUED FOR ALL DONATIONS MORE THAN $25.00.

A VOLUNTEER'S REPORT

I have worked voluntarily at the Women's Matrix for almost two years now. It is valuable and important to me for many reasons. First, it has given me the opportunity to be involved in a program that I see as making a real contribution to the lives of Latin American refugees and their families. I can see the results off my individual efforts and the Matrix's whole program as each participant develops, growns, and learning how to cope with the very real problems of accomodation and job searching in Canada. Secondly, I have been developing my own skills and gained experience in various capacites, rainging from E.S.L. teaching to advocacy work.

Thirdly, as a student who attends university, constantly drowning in books and more books, its a way of balancing theory and real life situations.

Last, and most importantly, volunteer work has been an opportunity to share challenges, laughter, learning, and (sometimes) tears with some very special and brave women.

The only problem I really see at the Women's Matrix is that the staff just have too much to do. There is not enough time or woman-power

20 to fulfill the responsibilities the Matrix has taken on. Volunteers contribute a great deal, nevertheless there should be more funding for paid staff, especially in employment placement, E.S.L., and for individual counselling. I know from experience how time-consuming this work is and can be. While I try to find a way to fit it into my life, I often must say No

25 because of other committments. Then I worry about the cancelation of some programs.

Sandi Eggleton

Job Placement

Last year witnessed the division of the W. M. Employment Division into two divisions: Employment Preparation and Job Placement. Division of one division into two in a one year time period has meant a continuous struggle to maintain an integrated approach in the face of perpetual time constraints and the structural tendencies which influence participants towards working separately. The past year has thereofre afforded us an interesting learning experience, and through the participants evaluations we have been able to develop a more comprehensive understanding of the kind and degree of information sharing and collaboration that is needed in the Employment Division. Parrallelling this has been a similar process of integration/collaboration involving the programme Divisions, such as the housing programme and the E.S.L. courses. In matching participants, especially from those Latin-American nations where literacy is anything but rampant, we are finding, increasinly, that the process of matching has to be simultaneously both more fluid and exact, as a result of the 'harmony' developing between the Employment and Programme Divisions.

Meanwhile, the W.M.'s profile among employers is continually increasing through the valuable efforts that volunteers and

50 Futures Trainees have directed into the Employment Division's efforts. Their work has greatly facilitated the job search process.

–Annabelle Hortense Crieff

Book-keeper's report

55   This is now the second time I am around to present the
relevant activities that have taken place in the
bookkeeping area in the Annual Report.

First of all, our accounting year changed from a July-
June period to a April-March accounting period.   This
60   change caused our books to be audited by our auditor
twice in the period 1987-1988!!!

The Womn's Matrix during this period, also moved
completely to Job Development funding under Canada
Manpower, and this program of the federal government
65   has become primary funder of The Women's Matrix. As per
standard government regulations for federally funded
agencies, they also required that an an audit be
submitted to them.

70   The Women's Matrix has been able to provide the
      participants of the program with a clothing allowance,
      a transportation allowance (one metropass/month) and
      day care for their children for the first six weeks.
      Moneys are not always readily available however, and
      sometimes I have to scramble to try and find fund for
75   these benefits. Fortunately, the Federal Government
      will now fund part of the clothing allowance, and the
      provincial government will pick up fifty percent of
      the child-care expenses

      submitted by Jeanette de Vaillancourt

COMMUNITY LIASON

The Women's Matrix has continued to develope links with other organizations that are concerned with refugees, women, employment, immigration and social issues. Some of the community activites that the Centre has participated in over the last year are:

1. Action for Refugee Men (organizing employment and community re-entry orientation programmes)

2. Curriculum input, the Canadian Council for Refugees.

3. Hispanic Council of Metro Toronto. Committee membership.

4. Signatory to petition by the National Action Committee on the Status of Women.

5. On the board of directors of the Ontario Council of Agencies Serving Immigrants.

6. Lobbied the provincial goverment on "no cutbacks in funding" for ESL.

7. Mental Health Task Force, Issues of Mental Health in Refugee Women.

PUBLIC FORUMS

100

1. One staff and one volunteer participated in the Metropolitan Toronto conference on refugee housing, sponsored
by the Refugee Documentation project of York University,
June '88.

2. Refugee Women, Breaking down the Barriers, an ex-
participant and a staff member participated as guest

105

panelists at a public forum at the univeristy of Toronto.

3. Jewish Family Services.

by Margaret Sunderland,

Community Liaison Coordinator.

ADMINISTRATIVE CO-ORDINATOR'S REPORT

110   The purpose of the administrative co-ordinator's report is to deal with the work which revolves around relationships with funders, with government regulations, and with the framework of support for its programs.

115   In 1987/88, that relations with funders shifted markedly. For instance, the Secretary of State of Canada used to give only small amounts of money to immigrant services for community projectss. Under a new program launched after a three-year campaign of

120 community pressure, they have now funded us as a long term financing operation, and increased their operating grant by 25% as well. And contrary to all rumours, the Canadian Immigration and Employment Commission maintained our employment placement program and agreed

125 to defray some of out other costs, such as the clothing allowance, which we offer the participants and the Metropass transportation assistance.

    As well, the CEIC also allowed us to admit women who had not spent 6 months unemployed yet.

130   On the other hand the Government has rammed through employability standards/education policy guidelines which have denied pending refugee status

claimants the right to access Ontario government job training programs. These unfortunate women are forced to take menial employment illegally to support themselves and their families, and to stay in over crowded and inadequate housing, while they wait for the government's ponderous processes to decide whether the situation that they have escaped from is dangerous enough to warrant a legitimate refugee status, and until they have that legitimacy, they are denied access to upgrading services that other residents of this country can take for granted.

Searching for more than a year, too, our childcare programs remain unfunded. Every government agency that we have approached, at both Federal and Provincial levels, has told us that the childcare needs of our participants are not their problem.

As we watch the government and press fan the flames or racism in Canada, we continue to try to build on the work we are doing at the Women's Matrix.

Andrea Smillie

Co-ordinator.

Recipes for Art

One of your favourite clients, an umbrella group for local arts organizations, asks you to copy edit its latest fund-raiser, a cookbook. A corporate sponsor will provide production on a sophisticated desktopping system, and a good designer is already at work. The recipes (donated by various arts figures) have been kitchen-tested and cleanly input. "The format works. But," confides the group's director, "I have a feeling the whole thing needs a commonsense edit."

Not being the world's most experienced cook, you hesitate. But a conversation with a friend who is a food editor persuades you to take the job. "It's fussy work but not really hard," she says. "Just remember you're looking for logic as well as consistency. You may have an advantage in not knowing a lot about cooking because you'll spot the places where the instructions are vague or incomplete. Let me jot down the things I look for."

Ingredients: Is the list complete and presented in the order of use?

Measurements: Do word order and punctuation distinguish between measuring ingredients "as purchased" (e.g., "1 cup mushrooms, sliced") and ingredients "as prepared" (e.g., "1 cup sliced mushrooms")?

Can the recipe be used easily by both "traditional" cooks (using cups, teaspoons, ounces) and "metric" cooks?

Preparation: Can you simplify the instructions (the cooking method) by including simple initial preparation in the ingredients list (e.g., 1 onion, chopped)?

Cooking method: Is each step mentioned in the order in which it occurs?

Have all steps been mentioned, including ones that are "obvious" to the experienced cook?

Utensils: Have cooking utensils been specified as they are required (e.g., "in a large saucepan," "with a wooden spoon")?

Does the cooking method help the cook to use as few utensils as possible (e.g., "in the same saucepan")?

Double-checks: Do the instructions deal with safety concerns (e.g., keeping cold things cold and hot things hot)?

Since cooking times depend on many factors (such as atmospheric pressure, humidity, differences in ingredients, and vagaries of the stove), is it clear what "doneness" looks, smells, or tastes like?

Steak, Oyster and Guiness Pie

1 lb	lean, cubed beef steak	500 g
1	veal kidney, trimmed of fat and cut into cubes	1
1 cup	Guiness beer	250 ml
1	large onion	1
2	bay leaves	2
1	thyme sprig	
1 tsp	tomato purée	15 ml
12	oysters, shucked	12
8 oz	puffed pastry	250 g
1	egg, beaten with 2 Tbsp (25 ml) water	1

1. Marinate beef and kidney in Guiness with chopped onion, bay leaves, thyme and tomato purée for several hours (covered).

2. Drain, reserving marinade, sprinkle with flour, stirring well. Add marinade juice and cook for 30 to 40 minutes. Allow to cool.

3. Drain mixture and place in four individual pie dishes. Add oysters.

4. Roll out puffed pastry to fit each pie. Brish with egg and water mixture and bake at 425°F for 25 minutes.

Creamy Tuna Pasta

Serves 4

8 oz	tubular pasta	250 g
1 cup	thawed frozen peas	250 mL
3 Tbsp	minced onion	45 mL
2 Tbsp	flour	25 mL
1 2/3 cups	whipping cream	400 mL
2 Tbsp	butter	25 mL
1 can	tuna, drained and broken into chunks	1 can
1/3 cup	green onions	75 mL
1/3 cup	fresh parsley or dill, chopped	75 mL
1/4 cup	Parmesan cheese	45 mL
	chopped parsley (for garnish)	

1. Sauté peas. Set aside. Cook pasta until done.

2. Meanwhile, melt butter. Add onion and cook until tender. Stir in flour and cook for a few seconds. Gradually whisk in milk and bring to simmer, stirring constantly until thickened. Whisk in remaining butter.

3. Add tuna, green onions, parsley or dill, and cheese. Pour over pasta and stir gently to mix. Serve immediately.

Pork Tenderloin Wrapped in Prosciutto with
Dill-Asparagus Sauce
Serves four
1 1/2 lb   pork tenderloin trimmed of fat
5   2 Tbsp   olive oil
            salt and pepper
8   slices prosciutto

Dill Asparagus Sauce
10   1/2 cup   white wine
1/2 cup   chicken stock
2   shallots, thinly sliced
2 cups   peeled chopped asparaugs
4   sprigs of dill, shredded
15   1/2 cup   whipping cream
            lemon juice to taste

Cut pork into four equal portions. Rub
with olive oil and sprinkle with salt and
pepper. Wrap each portion with two slices
20   prosciutto.
Boil wine, stock and shallots gently
until liquid is reduced by half. Add
asparagus. Cook until soft.
Purée sauce in blender or food
25   processor; return to stove. Stir in cream and
lemon juice. Bring to boil, strain through a
fine sieve and serve.

A Table for a Friend

When you arrive to pick up a friend for a visit to that new Thai restaurant, you find her still at her desk. "I'm sorry," she says. "The economics papers I'm editing for that archival series are due tomorrow, and it's taking longer than I expected. I still have a couple of hours of work here."

You know little about economics, but you were looking forward to that dinner. "Anything I can do to help?" you ask.

"Yes," she replies. "Unlike a lot of these articles, this piece has just one table. It doesn't contradict the text in any way, but it sure needs tidying up. Would you copy edit it and mark it up?"

She hands you the single page of manuscript. "If you have queries for the author—and you probably will—I think there's room to write them on the page." In lieu of a style sheet, she finds a table in a previous publication from the same publisher. On it she jots the markup codes.

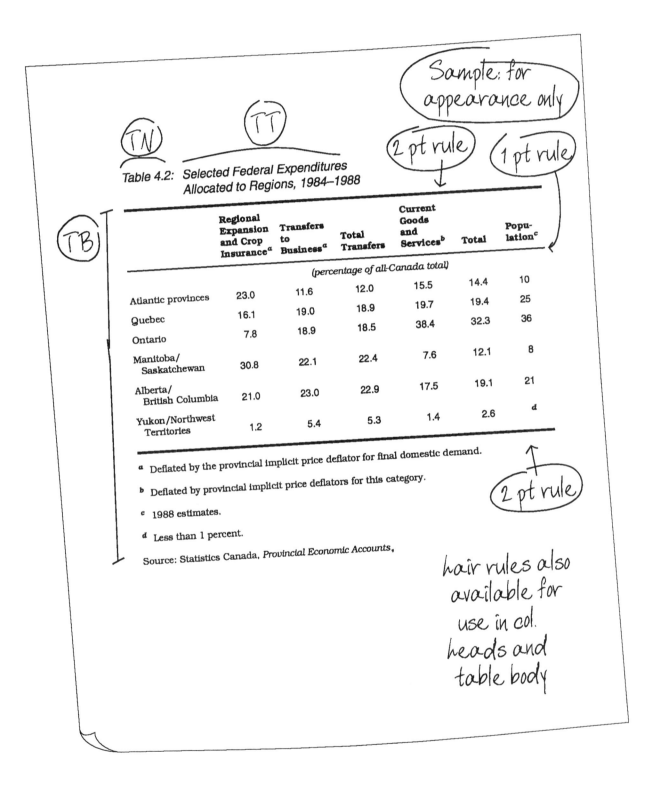

Sample: for appearance only

2 pt rule

1 pt rule

Table 4.2: Selected Federal Expenditures Allocated to Regions, 1984–1988

	Regional Expansion and Crop Insurance[a]	Transfers to Business[a]	Total Transfers	Current Goods and Services[b]	Total	Population[c]
(percentage of all-Canada total)						
Atlantic provinces	23.0	11.6	12.0	15.5	14.4	10
Quebec	16.1	19.0	18.9	19.7	19.4	25
Ontario	7.8	18.9	18.5	38.4	32.3	36
Manitoba/ Saskatchewan	30.8	22.1	22.4	7.6	12.1	8
Alberta/ British Columbia	21.0	23.0	22.9	17.5	19.1	21
Yukon/Northwest Territories	1.2	5.4	5.3	1.4	2.6	[d]

[a] Deflated by the provincial implicit price deflator for final domestic demand.

[b] Deflated by provincial implicit price deflators for this category.

[c] 1988 estimates.

[d] Less than 1 percent.

Source: Statistics Canada, *Provincial Economic Accounts*.

2 pt rule

hair rules also available for use in col. heads and table body

Table #

Various Sources of revenue To The Canadian Federal
Government, Canada, Actual Data For 1982-1983, Estimated
For 1984, Projected Data for 1985-87

	1982/83	1983/84	1984/85	1985/86	1986/87
	$ billions	$ billions	$billions	$billions	$billions
Taxing personal incomes	24	26.3	28.3	32.8	17
Taxing Corporations	8.1	7.1	7.8	9.8	10.3
Energy Tax	3.3	4	3.7	3.9	4.0
Social Insurance Premiums	6.4	6.6	9.1	10.2	11.6
Federal Sales Tax	6.2	5.9	6.6	7.3	8.8
Income from federal govt making	5.6	6.6	6.8	7	7.7
investments Others	11.6	10.2	10.7	11.5	13.9
	65.2	66.7	74.9	82.5	93.3

"Other" data includes adjustments to Natl Accounts. Totals are on a
National Accounts basis.

Source: Dept of Finance, The Fiscal Plan (Ottawa, February 1984). p, 9,
11, 40

The Dean's List

You receive a telephone call from the associate dean of social sciences of a nearby university. The school is going to publish the proceedings of a conference on the prevention of mental illness, which it co-sponsored last year. The papers are being edited by a research assistant, but he is falling behind and is going to need some help, says the dean.

She asks if you would tackle a bibliography for a paper written by three authors. She clearly knows a lot about editing. You accept the challenge.

"What style do you want?" you ask.

"We're using author-date citations, but we haven't set a bibliography style yet," she replies. "I've been impressed with the National Library of Canada's style as adapted in *Editing Canadian English*. But if you don't have a copy of that handy, you could just follow *The Chicago Manual*'s style for that system."

You're not surprised to find out there's some hurry. "All the authors are theoretically available for queries," explains the dean, "but we've worked mostly with one of them and she will be in town only one day next week to answer your queries."

References

Akiskal, Hagop S. (1989.) "New Insights into the Nature and Heterogeneity of Mood Disorders." <u>Journal of Clinical Psychiatry</u> 50(5, supplement): 6-12.

Arngrim, Torben. 1975. Attempted Suicide: Etiology and Long Term Prognosis-A Follow-up Study. Denmark: Odense University Press.

Belle, Deborah. ed. 1982. Lives in Stress: Women and Depression. Beverly Hills, Calif.: Sage. 2nd ed.

Belle, Debora; Goldman, Noreen. 1980. Patterns of Diagnoses Received by Men and Women. In Guttentag, Marcia; Salasin, Susan; Belle, Deborah, eds., The Mental Health of Women. New York: Academic Press, pp.21-30.

Chesler, Phyllis. Women and Madness. New York: Doubleday.

Cobb, Bruce Ward. 1991. "Controversial Suicide

Manual a Best-Seller. _The Cambridge Reporter_. 17
August 1991. Weekend Observer, p. B3.

Cohen, Yehudi A. 1961. "The Sociological
Relevance of Schizophrenia and Depression." In
his Social Structure and Personality: A Casebook.
New York: Holt, Rinehart and Winston, pp. 477-
485.

Eaton, William W. _et al_. 1989. "Major Depressive
Disorder in the Community: A Latent Class
Analysis of Data from the NIMH Epidemiologic
Catchment Area Programme." British Journal of
Psychiatry 155(2)(May/June 1989):48-54.

Ettlinger, R. 1980. "A Follow-up Investigation of
Patients after Attempted Suicide." In Richard
Farmer and Steven Hirsch, eds., _The Suicide
Syndrome_. London: Croom Helm, pp. 167-72.

Farmer, Richard. 1980a. The Difference between
Those Who Repeat and Those Who Do Not. In _The
Suicide Syndrome_, Richard Farmer and Steven
Hirsch, eds. London: Croom Helm, pp. 19-37.

-- 1980b. The Relationship between Suicide and
Parasuicide. In The Suicide Syndrome. Richard
Farmer and Steven Hirsch, eds. London: Croom
Helm, pp. 19-37.

-- and Hirsch, Steven, ed., 1980, The Suicide
Syndrome (London: Croom Helm,   ).

Freedman, Alfred M. (1989),"Overview: Depression
in Health and Illness," Journal of Clinical
Psychiatry 50(5-Supplement): 3-5.

Katschnig, H.; Sint, P.; and Fuchs-Robetin, G.
1980. "Suicide and Parasuicide: Identification of
High- and Low-Risk Groups by Cluster Analysis."
In Farmer and Hirsch, pp. 154-166.

Lefebvre, L.A.; Adams, O. B. 1980. Retirement and
Mortality: An Examination of Mortality in a Group
of Retired Canadians. Occasional Paper, cat. no.
83-521E. Ottawa: Statistics Canada.

Lester, David. 1987. Suicide as a Learned
Behavior. Springfield, IL: Charles C. Thomas.

Lester, David. 2003. A Regional Analysis of Suicide Rates in the USA. *Journal of Social Psychiatry and Psychiatric Epidemiology.* Forthcoming.

Lewinsohn, Peter M.; Zeiss, Antoinette M.; and Duncan, Edward M. 1989. Probability of relapse after recovery from an episode of depression. Journal of Abnormal Psychology 98(2): 107-116.

Makosky, Vivian Parker. 1980. "Stress and the Mental Health of Women: A Discussion of Research and Issues." In The Mental Health of Women. Marcia Guttentag, Susan Salasin, and Deborah Belle, eds. New York: Academic Press, pp. 111-27.

Makosky, Vivian Parker. 1982. Sources of Stress: Events or Conditions? In Lives in Stress:Women and Depression. Ed. by Deborah Belle. Beverly Hills, CA: Sage, pp. 35-53.

Miller, Suzanne M. 1980. In Human Helplessness: Theory and Applications. Judy Garber and Martin E.P. Seligman, eds. New York: Academic Press, pp. 71-96.

Oakley, Ann. 1981. Interviewing Women: A
Contradiction in Terms. In Helen Roberts,
ed.,Doing Feminist Research. London: Routledge &
105   Kegan Paul, pp. 39-85.

Paykel, E.S. 1980. A Classification of Suicide
Attempters by Cluster Analysis. In Farmer and
Hirsch, pp. 144-153.

110

Paykel, E.S. 1980. Recent Life Events and
Attempted Suicide. In Farmer and Hirsch, pp.
105-115.

115   The Reason To Live: A Special Report on Youth
Suicide. 1987. Produced by Sally Armstrong and
Canadian Living magazine. Toronto. Video
distributed by Canadian Living. Based on research
for an article of the same title, by Armstrong,
120   in Canadian Living magazine, March 21, 1987, pp.
39-40 42, 44, 46, 48.

Rose, A.M. 1962. A Social-Psychological Theory of
Neurosis. In Human Behaviour and Social

125 Processes. A.M. Rose, ed. London: Routlege and

Kegan Paul, pp. 45-79.

Rossiter, Amy. 1988. From Public to Private: A

Feminist Exploration of Mothering. Toronto: Woman

130 Press.

Solursh, Diane, 1987. Director. Suicide in

Canada: Report of the National Task Force on

Suicide . Health and Welfare Canada, Ottawa.

135 Listed herein as NTFS.

Statistics Canada. Living Alone in Canada:

Demographic and Econmic Perspectives, 1951-76. By

Brian R. Harrison. Statistics Canada occasional

140 paper, catalogue no. 98-811. Ottawa: Statistics

Canada, [1979].

Statistics Canada. 1990. Vital Statistics, 1990,

Vol. 1. Births and Deaths, 1990. Ottawa:

145 Statistics Canada. cat. 84-204.

Stephens, B. Joyce. 1985. Suicidal women and

their relationships with husbands, boyfriends,

and lovers. Suicide and Life-threatening Behavior

15(2).

150

Tombs, T.P. 1965. Trends in Suicidal Behaviour: A
Sociological and Psychological Study. Edmonton:
Diocese of Edmonton, Council of Social Service,
The Anglican Church of Canada.

155

van Dalen, Helene; Jackson, Anna. "Suicidal Behavior,"
Practice and Research, Journal of the Center for the Study
of Social Work Practice, Columbia University School of
Social Work. Website at www.columbia.edu/cu/csswp/
160 journal/news1997/suicidal.html.

Waterhouse, John, and Platt, Stephen. "General
Hospital Admission in the Management of
Parasuicide: A Randomised Controlled Trial.
British Journal of Psychiatry :236-242.
165

See also
Eldrid, John. 1988. Caring for the Suicidal.
London: Constable.

170

Taylor, Steve. 1988. The Sociology of Suicide.
London: Longman.

Markup in a Hurry

You receive the following e-mail from the head of college production at a large educational publishing company. In a weak moment, you agree to help out this harassed client. The following pages contain one of the forty chapters you receive by courier the next day.

Sue ▯□✕

File Edit View Tools Help

Subject: | Markup in a Hurry   Priority: | Normal ▾

Hi. Are you busy these days? We're almost ready to go to type with an advanced text -- a huge thing with chapters by various authors. The copy editor has been called out of town for a family emergency. He's completed all the editing onscreen, and has dealt with the authors' responses to queries. The final step he didn't get around to was marking up the manuscript for the formatter. Could you take on this task?

We're already a week behind schedule and it's a long book, but you would only have to mark the codes on hard copy. We have two interns who can key them in. I don't have a design sample yet -- guess what else is behind schedule? But I can give you a list of the elements and the codes to use.

Please let me know ASAP if you can take this on.

Sue

P.S. Just remembered one more thing. At the end of each chapter is a list of key terms. They're going to appear in the margins of the textbook, each one right beside where the word is first defined. The copy editor was supposed to mark their position at the markup stage. Can you do that too?

Design Elements
Smith/Jones, Health Care
17 April 2001

P	"Part"		FN	footnote
PN	part number		SN	"Case" and number
PTT	part title		SH	case head
PT	part opener text		ST	case text
RH	running head		SL	list in case
C	"Chapter"		SQ	case questions
CN	chapter number		SS	case source OR case note
CTT	chapter title		IBS	"It's Been Said" logo (goes with text boxes)
T	main text		BH	box head
L	lists in text		BT	box text
H-1	text subhead first level		BS	box source
H-2	text subhead second level			
H-3	text subhead third level			
H-4	text subhead fourth level			
EX	extract			
KT	key terms			

Part 2

VOICES FROM THE FIELD

All health care situations are not equal. Many present particular, difficult problems for caregivers.

5   The next two chapters deal with some common but complex situations. In this section, we shall hear from practitioners and researchers who have been dealing with particular kinds of health care problems, such as chronic illness, terminal illness, and emergencies. In the next chapter, the focus will switch to particular kinds of patients, including children, the elderly, and sole heads of
10 families (usually women).

[Part 2 includes chapters 5/6/7]

[Chap 5 running heads:

verso – Voices from the Field

recto – Living with Chronic Illness]

[UNNUMBERED FOOTNOTE:] Dr. McDade is a member of the Department of Psychology at the University of Melbourne. While serving as a visiting lecturer at Dalhousie University, she wrote this paper, for which she gratefully acknowledges the support of a grant from the Ellen Daly Foundation.

Chapter 5 Living with Chronic Illness

by Catherine McDade

1.0 Introduction

Having to live with chronic illness has been part of human experience since prehistory. Only recently, however, has it become a closely studied phenomenon, one of interest to physical and mental health scientists, sociologists, and economists, not to mention patients and their families. They are trying to discover how the increasing number of sufferers can be helped to live happy and productive lives.

2.0 What Is Chronic Illness?

The first step in studying any phenomenon is to define the subject. *Chronic illness* is a familiar term, one that tempts everyone to say, "Of course I know what that is." Yet do you?

2.1 What Is Illness?

People often have difficulty even defining *illness*. Many find it easiest to use antonyms, contrasting the word with *health*. More subtle analysts also contrast it with *disease*.

2.1.1.1 Illness As Opposed to Health

Tatham concerns himself with a condition he calls "un-health," which "is reckoned to be a bad, noxious, or troublesome condition" (Tatham 1998, p. 23). The word *health*, he continues, is

cognate with wholeness, which means complete. . . . Health is not the same thing as . . . that ultimate wholeness to which humans aspire. . . . There is, however, a formal wholeness, . . . which continuously changes and outgrows its prior state, to provide new "wholenesses." These changing states . . . are experienced as moments of feeling integrated. . . . In these terms a healthy person is not necessarily whole . . . and may be leading a highly one-sided and unintegrated life. Equally, a sick or diseased person can achieve a certain wholeness, by accepting the illness as an integral part of her- or himself. . . . Thus, [un-health can be understood as] an individual style of being healthy which helps to make me whole, and which I shall undergo from time to time. (p. 24)

Kleinman (1998), on the other hand, offers a useful definition of *illness*, though he casts a wide net:

The term illness [means] the innately human experience of symptoms and suffering. Illness refers to how the sick person and the members of the

55 wider social network perceive, live with and respond to symptoms and
    disability. Illness is the lived experience. The illness experience includes
    categorizing and explaining . . . the forms of distress caused by the
    pathophysiological process. (pp. 3–4)

2.1.1.2   Illness as opposed to disease

60 What Kleinman is leading up to is a distinction that appears in much current
    literature on health issues: the difference between *illness* and *disease*. As he puts
    it: "Disease . . . is what the practitioner creates in . . . recasting illness in
    terms of theories of disorder."

    Kane (1991), like many others, says the distinction is crucial because
65   Cancer (arthritis/lupus/migraines/whatever) never bothered
            anyone. . . . What bothers people with cancer, for example, is not
            the tumor or any disorder of function, but their own experience of it:
            fear, pain, guilt, depression, anxiety, despair, and so on. If the
            disease didn't exist, neither would the illness, but that doesn't mean
70   they are the same. (p. 14)

    In completing his list of distinctions, Kane adds another useful term:

    • *Sickness:* The process of "disease" and "illness." If sickness were a coin,
      disease and illness would be "heads" and "tails."

- *Disease:* The physical, objectively measurable aspect of sickness. This is what doctors are trained to diagnose and treat.

- *Illness:* Your subjective, unmeasurable experience of the disease; the sum of your suffering. (Kane 1991, p. 13)

2.1.2 Chronic Illness

A person who has had a chronic illness has a sickness that can never be pronounced cured, although it may be experienced in varying degrees over time. As one useful definition says, *chronic illness* is

The irreversible presence, accumulation, or latency of disease states or impairments that involve the total human environment for supportive care and self-care, maintenance of function and prevention of further disability. (Curtin and Lubkin 1990, p. 6)

3 The Prevalence of Chronical Illness

Research presents a "picture of increasing strain — for families, the medical care system, social services and the economy — associated with levels of chronic illness in the population (Anderson and Bury 1998, p. 4). Chronic illness seems to be increasing. Nobody knows the exact number of people affected — studies give varying results because of problems of definition and measurement — but a common estimate is that chronic illness and disabilities affect about one-tenth of the adult population (ibid., p. 5). The reason for the increase is twofold:

95   1.   The success of modern technology, including health care. Register comments ruefully:

> Chronic illness is . . . a sign of progress. Had we lived a century ago . . ., many of us who are chronically ill would not be alive at thirty or forty or fifty. Earlier and more precise diagnosis, more effective remedies against acute problems, and better means of maintaining health have slowed the course and limited the impact of some diseases that used to be quickly terminal. (Register 1997, p. ix)

100

2.   The aging of the population. Even if the incidence rate is unchanging, any rise in the average age guarantees a rise in the absolute number of chronically ill individuals.

105

4.0 Learning to Live with It

More and more people are surviving more and more conditions that once might have killed them. These individuals, their families, health care workers, and all society face a problem. Register says:

110   As more and more people learn to live hopefully and purposely with the daily awareness of interminable disease, popular notions about the experience of illness are . . . challenged. People can and do find ways to accommodate physical and mental illness without either denying it or letting it govern their lives. (Ibid.)

115 But anyone who must live with a chronic illness can appreciate the difficulty of achieving that balanced state Register describes so succinctly. It's rather like being told by a baseball coach, "Just hit the ball squarely." You know what you're supposed to do, you want to do it, but you haven't any idea exactly how to go about doing it.

120 [CATCH: Box 5-1]

[Box 6.1]

It's Been Said

Acceptance and Surrender

There is much you can do toward achieving a healing attitude. To be exact, you can move toward accepting your disease. . . .

Acceptance is not the same as pessimistic resignation to your disease. On the other hand, it doesn't necessarily mean you'll be cured of it. In short, acceptance has nothing to do with the future. It's simply an acknowledgement of the incontrovertible present. . . .

You know that feisty folks do better at surviving illness with a relatively higher quality of life, but on the other hand people like me suggest that you continue to "accept" your sickness. So which should you do, fight or surrender?

Both.

Fight versus surrender is, in fact, a false distinction. Opting exclusively for either will dilute your effort, because flight and surrender are complementary. . . .

To act powerfully, first surrender. Only when you have accepted your sickness — feel relaxed in its presence — can you formulate a realistic fight plan. Short of this, fear and anxiety will generate jagged, half-hearted responses, and you'll waste valuable energy on impossible quests.

145

150

The mind . . . constantly reiterates its litany of stability. It resists all change. . . . So your mind will insist that you'd rather not be sick, you don't want to die, you'd like your old life back, and so on, typically heedless of reality. Universal as it is, this is a kind of tail-chasing that cannot but wear you out. . . . Many people have described their illness to me as the most harrowing and the most educational adventure of their lives. [Said one], "Pain is inevitable; suffering is optional."

Source: Jeff Kane. *Be Sick Well: A Healthy Approach to Chronic Illness* (Oakland, Calif.: New Harbinger, 1991), 41–42, 50–52.

References

Anderson, Robert, and Michael Bury. 1998. "Introduction," in *Living with Chronic Illness: The Experience of Patients and Their Families*, ed. by R. Anderson and M. Bury. London: Unwin Hyman.

155 Curtin, Mary, and Ilene Lubkin. 1990. "What Is Chronicity?" in *Chronic Illness: Impact and Interventions*, 2d ed., ed. by I. Lubkin. Boston: Jones and Bartlett.

Kane, Jeff. 1991. *Be Sick Well: A Healthy Approach to Chronic Illness*. Oakland, Calif.: New Harbinger.

160 Healthy People 2010 Web site. 2000. <web.health.gov/healthypeople/>.

Kleinman, Arthur. 1998. *The Illness Narratives: Suffering, Healing, and the Human Condition*. New York: Basic Books.

National Center for Chronic Disease Prevention and Health Promotion (NCCDPHP). 2000. "About Chronic Disease." <http://www.cdc.gov/nccdphp/about.htm>.

165

Register, Cheri. 1997. *Living with Chronic Illness: Days of Patience and Passion*. New York: Bantam Books.

Tatham, Peter. 1998. "Items and Motion," in *The Meaning of Illness*, ed. by M. Kidel and S. Rowe-Leete. London: Routledge.

170 [Key Terms for chapter 5 -- to appear in margins beside first place term is defined; placement will be marked on hard copy:
Illness
Disease
Sickness
175 Chronic Illness]

Proofreading

The proofreader usually carries out the last inspection of a document before it is published or distributed. This imposes a particular responsibility to correct errors originating in any prior stage of the document's preparation. It may also allow the advantage (even the pleasure) of reading a document that has arrived nearly in the form in which its intended readers will see it, of reading it at close to a normal rate, and of paying attention to many of the same things that a regular reader does.

Although proofreaders are often asked to "read to copy", the task is seldom as mechanical as suggested by that simple instruction. Judgment comes into play. Are there errors or faults best left uncorrected? What expenses should be incurred and what time taken at a stage in the project where both are often severely limited? And if budget and schedule do allow for editorial changes at the proof stage, how much should a proofreader feel free to correct and how much should be queried?

It is important for the proofreader to know how to defer to established style in a document. Differences of opinion with the editor should not automatically lead to re-editing or a flurry of queries. In cases where the style is not set out explicitly, the proofreader needs to know how to recognize a document's established style by looking for patterns and making inferences. The proofreader must also be aware of inconsistencies in the style and be able to make the text conform to the style that has been asked for or, lacking that, the style that predominates and is appropriate for the project. Only one of the exercises in this section includes an editorial style sheet; all of them place a premium on your judgment and discretion.

A proofreader has responsibility for both the textual and visual elements of the finished document. The proofreader is therefore required to look at the entire visual effect and must be able to understand and apply design specifications. Sometimes the interplay of text and design raises problems that can only be solved through a complete understanding of the proofreader's mandate and the purpose of the document.

The scenarios that open the following exercises will help you to determine your mandate and the room for decision making in various proofreading situations.

Test Report

You have been asked to proofread the first page proofs of a product report for an audiophile magazine. The material was keyed by a word-processing operator (who took down a few last-minute changes over the telephone) before being sent to the typesetter. Because this is your first job for this magazine, the managing editor has sent you the house style sheet along with the manuscript and the typesetter's first page proofs. You find the style sheet a little skimpy, given the technical terminology that litters the pages of the magazine. That, you reflect, can be put down to the fact that most of the editorial work at *Sound Decisions* is done in-house by editors who are familiar with the subject.

Note: The magazine's style sheet is on pages 138–139, the proofs for you to work on are on pages 140–142, and the manuscript is on pages 143–147.

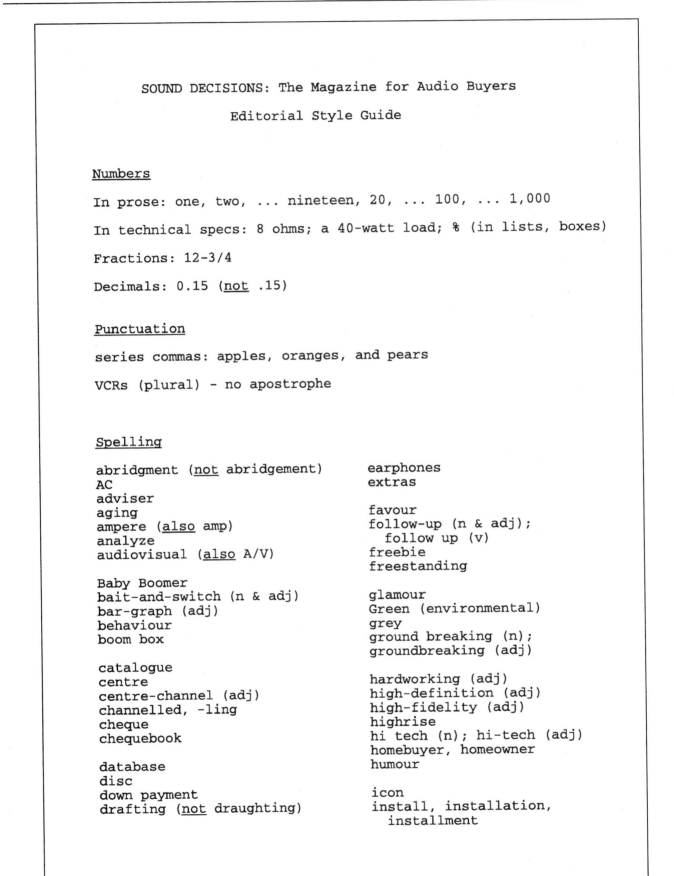

SOUND DECISIONS: The Magazine for Audio Buyers

Editorial Style Guide

Numbers

In prose: one, two, ... nineteen, 20, ... 100, ... 1,000

In technical specs: 8 ohms; a 40-watt load; % (in lists, boxes)

Fractions: 12-3/4

Decimals: 0.15 (not .15)

Punctuation

series commas: apples, oranges, and pears

VCRs (plural) - no apostrophe

Spelling

abridgment (not abridgement)
AC
adviser
aging
ampere (also amp)
analyze
audiovisual (also A/V)

Baby Boomer
bait-and-switch (n & adj)
bar-graph (adj)
behaviour
boom box

catalogue
centre
centre-channel (adj)
channelled, -ling
cheque
chequebook

database
disc
down payment
drafting (not draughting)

earphones
extras

favour
follow-up (n & adj);
 follow up (v)
freebie
freestanding

glamour
Green (environmental)
grey
ground breaking (n);
groundbreaking (adj)

hardworking (adj)
high-definition (adj)
high-fidelity (adj)
highrise
hi tech (n); hi-tech (adj)
homebuyer, homeowner
humour

icon
install, installation,
 installment

jacks
judgment

licence (n); license (v)
lifestyle (n, adj)
livable
long-term (adj)

mail order (n);
  mail-order (adj)
markup
marvellous
meter (instrument for
  measuring)
metre (unit of measure)
microchip
midrange
motor-driven

nanometre
no one

ohm
old-time (adj)
overall (adj)
overdub
overload

parallel, -led
passerby
percent
playback
power amp
preamplifier but pre-amp
preset
pre-supplied
program
proprietary

remote-control (adj)
risk-taking (n, adj)

salable
sales figures
secondhand
sizable
skeptic
skilful
sound-field (n & adj)
soundtrack
stereophonic
sub-woofer

tape deck
tariff
tax-exempt
tone control (n);
  tone-control (adj)
trademark
TV
tweeter

up-market
upscale

videodisc
volt

watt

TEST REPORT •

The E-SV810PRO, Energumen's latest surround-sound audio/-video integrated amplifier, features Dolby Pro Logic decoding for Dolby Surround sound tracks and digital signal-processing (DSP) circuitry for ambiance enhancement of music. It features as well five power amplifiers. Three are rated to deliver 85 watts each to left and right front and centre speakers, and two are rated for 35 watts each to a pair of rear speakers (all based on 8-ohm loads).

The E-SV810PRO provides ten factory-preset surround modes selectable via five front-panel buttons. These buttons can additionally be used to select from another ten used-programmed DPP sound fields. The adjustable parameters include treble, midrange, and bass frequency response and level for each of the five channels, the overall level of the sound-field effects, simulated room size and shape and reverbration level. Although these adjustments can be made using the front-panel controls and display, they are most efficiently executed by using the pre-supplied remote control and the on-screen displays on a TV connected to the monitor. Connection is made with the output in the rear of the amplifier.

The E-SV810PRO has rear-apron audio inputs for a CD player, tuner, and moving-magnet phono cartridge as well as recording and playback connectors for a single audio tape deck. There are audio and video connectors for three VCR's and playback inputs for a videodisc player and a direct-broadcast satellite (DBS) receiver. Each video circuit includes an S-video connector in addition to a coaxial connector for composite video.

The speaker outputs at the rear of the receiver are insulated binding posts compatible with dual bananna plugs. They accommodate left and right front speakers, either one or two centre-channel speakers, and two rear surround speakers. In contrast with most integrated amplifiers and receivers, the E-SV81OPRO does not provide an extra set of outputs for a pair of speakers in another room. Left and right line-level outputs drive a sub-woofer through a separate amplifier. The three AC outlets are switched.

Considering the complexity and versatility of the E-SV810PRO, its front panel is strikingly simple and uncluttered. A large display window dominates the centre of the panel, with a volume knob to one side. (The knob is motor-driven when the remote control is used.) Normally, the display shows the selected program source in large letters; small blue lights identify the surround mode in use. A cluster of of bar-graph displays shows the tone-control settings of all five channels.

The Energumen E-SV810PRO is a large amplifier, meas uring 18 inches wide, 16-1/2 inches deep, and 6-3/4 inches high and it weighs about 36=1/3 pounds. The front panel's edges feature an attractive turquoise trim, and the unit is finished in white with metallic grey markings. Price: $1,355. Energuman, Dept SR, 3230-A Oak Ridges, Unit 5A, Markhan, ON L3R 2B6.

Select Laboratory Measurements

- 1,000-HZ output power at clipping: main front channels (both driven), 90 watts into 8 ohms, 104 watts into 4 ohms; center channel (driven alone), 104 watts into 4 ohms; rear channels (both driven), 40 watts into 8 ohms
- clipping headroom: main front, 0.25 dB (8 ohms referred to 85 watts); centre, 0.88 dB (8 ohms referred to 35 watts); rear, 0.58 dB (8 ohms referred to 35 watts);
- Dynamic power output: main front, 92 watts into 8 ohms, 157 watts into 4 ohms, 225 watts in 2 ohms
- Maximum distortion (20 t0 20,000 Hz into 8 ohms): 0.6% at 20 HZ and 85 watts; 0.06% from 40 to 20,000 Hz
- Sensitivity: (for a 1-watt output into 8 ohms): CD, 40 mV; phono, 0.7 mV

Laboratory Tests

The Energumen E-SV810PRO delivered a clipping-level power output of 90 watts into 8-ohm loads, with both channels driving, at 1,000 Hz in the bypass setting. Although it is not rated for loads of less than 6 ohms our measurement into 4

75 ohms showed an output of 140 watts at clipping, with no consequent damage to the amplifier or even activation of its overload protection. The dynamic power output of the three front channels at clipping was 92 watts each into 8 ohms, 157 watts into 4 ohms, and 225 watts into 2 ohms. Total

80 harmonic distortion plus noise (THD + N), in the front channels was less than 0.03 percent from 20 to 80 watts. Frequency response, through the CD inputs, was +0, 0.1 db from 20 to 20,000 Hz. The RIAA equalization error of the phono preamplifier was essentially zero from 20,000 t0 1,000

85 Hz, rising to +1.4 dB at 20 Hz.

Sound Decisions

Comments

Despite the considerable combined power capability of its five amplifers, the E-SV810PRO never became dangerously hot,

90 even when operated into 4-ohm loads. Its protective systems provided ample margin for error.

This is a very versatile component. Its appearance is deceptively simple: although it can be used to full effect entirely through the front panel controls, its remote control

95 option offers marked advantages in adjustment from the listening position with the listener viewing its surround-ad-justment menus on a video monitor. The E-SV810PRO, when integrated in a four-speaker surround-sound system, was as least as effective in creating a believable sonic field as other

100 surround processors we have used. A minor disadvantage may be its size and weight; last month we reviewed a comparable amplifier that weighed in at only 28½ pounds. But not everyone will find fault with its bulk. Assuming that your other system components are compatible Energumen or

105 similar models, this fine amplifier/control centre can anchor a versatile and outstandingly easy-to-operate A/V system.

TEST REPORT

The E-SV810PRO, Energumen's latest surround-sound audio/video integrated amplifier, features Dolby Pro Logic decoding for Dolby Surround soundtracks and digital signal-processing (DSP) circuitry for ambiance enhancement of music. It features as well five power amplifiers. Three are rated to deliver 85 watts each to left and right front and centre speakers, and two are rated for 35 watts each to a pair of rear speakers (all based on 8-ohm loads).

The E-SV810PRO provides ten factory-preset surround modes selectable via five front-panel buttons. These buttons can additionally be used to select from another ten user-programmed DSP sound fields. The adjustable parameters include treble, midrange, and bass frequency response and level for each of the five channels, the overall level of the sound-field effects, simulated room size and shape, and reverberation level. Although these adjustments can be made using the front-panel controls and display, they are most efficiently executed by using the pre-supplied remote control and the on-screen displays on a TV connected to the monitor. Connection is made with the output in the rear of the amplifier.

The E-SV810PRO has rear-apron audio inputs for a CD player, tuner, and moving-magnet phono cartridge as well as recording and playback connectors for a single audio tape deck. There are audio and video connectors for three VCRs and playback inputs for a

25 videodisc player and a direct-broadcast satellite (DBS) receiver.
Each video circuit includes an S-video connector in addition to a
coaxial connector for composite video.

The speaker outputs at the rear of the receiver are insulated
binding posts compatible with dual banana plugs. They accommodate
30 left and right front speakers, either one or two centre-channel
speakers, and two rear surround speakers. In contrast with most
integrated amplifiers and receivers, the E-SV810PRO does not
provide an extra set of outputs for a pair of speakers in another
room. Left and right line-level outputs drive a sub-woofer through
35 a separate amplifier. The three AC outlets are switched.

Considering the complexity and versatility of the E-SV810PRO,
its front panel is strikingly simple and uncluttered. A large
display window dominates the centre of the panel, with a volume
knob to one side. (The knob is motor-driven when the remote
40 control is used.) Normally, the display shows the selected
program source in large letters; small blue lights identify the
surround mode in use. A cluster of bar-graph displays shows the
tone-control settings of all five channels.

The Energumen E-SV810PRO is a large amplifier, measuring 18
45 inches wide, 16-1/2 inches deep, and 6-3/4 inches high and it
weighs about 36-1/2 pounds. The front panel's edges feature an
attractive turquoise trim, and the unit is finished in white with

metallic grey markings. Price: '$1,355. Energumen, Dept. SR, 3230-A

Oak Ridges, Unit 5A, Markham, ON L3R 2B6.

50

Selected Laboratory Measurements

* 1,000-Hz output power at clipping: main front channels (both

driven), 90 watts into 8 ohms, 130 watts into 4 ohms; centre

channel (driven alone), 104 watts into 4 ohms; rear channels (both

driven), 40 watts into 8 ohms

55

* clipping headroom: main front, 0.25 dB (8 ohms referred to 85

watts); centre, 0.88 dB (8 ohms referred to 85 watts); rear, 0.58

dB (8 ohms referred to 35 watts);

* Dynamic power output: main front, 92 watts into 8 ohms, 157

watts into 4 ohms, 225 watts into 2 ohms

60

* Maximum distortion (20 to 20,000 Hz into 8 ohms): 0.6% at 20 HZ

and 85 watts; 0.06% from 40 to 20,000 Hz

* Sensitivity: (for a 1-watt output into 8 ohms): CD, 40 mV;

phono, 0.7 mV

Laboratory Tests

65

The Energumen E-SV810PRO delivered a clipping-level power output

of 90 watts into 8-ohm loads, with both channels driven, at 1,000

Hz in the bypass setting. Although it is not rated for loads of

less than 6 ohms, our measurement into 4 ohms showed an output of

140 watts at clipping, with no consequent damage to the amplifier

70   or even activation of its overload protection. The dynamic power

output of the three front channels at clipping was 92 watts each

into 8 ohms, 157 watts into 4 ohms, and 225 watts into 2 ohms.

Total harmonic distortion plus noise (THD + N) in the front

channels was less than 0.03 percent from 20 to 80 watts. Frequency

75   response, through the CD inputs, was +0, -0.1 dB from 20 to 20,000

Hz. The RIAA equalization error of the phono preamplifier was

essentially zero from 20,000 to 1,000 Hz, rising to +1.4 dB at 20

Hz.

Sound Decisions

Comments

80   Despite the considerable combined power capability of its five

amplifiers, the E-SV810PRO never became dangerously hot, even when

operated into 4-ohm loads. Its protective system provided ample

margin for error.

85   This is a very versatile component. Its appearance is

deceptively simple: although it can be used to full effect

entirely through the front panel controls, its remote-control

option offers marked advantages in adjustment from the listening

position with the listener viewing its surround-adjustment menus

90   on a video monitor. The E-SV810PRO, when integrated in a four-

speaker surround-sound system, was at least as effective in

creating a believable sonic field as other surround processors we

95 | have used. A minor disadvantage may be its size and weight; last month we reviewed a comparable amplifier that weighed in at only 28 1/2 pounds. But not everyone will find fault with its bulk. Assuming that your other system components are compatible Energumen or similar models, this fine amplifier/control centre can anchor a versatile and outstandingly easy-to-operate A/V system.

Acid Rain

You have been asked by a small publishing house to proofread the galleys for its first book. You learn that the manuscript was copy edited by the managing editor and the keying was the responsibility of the typesetter.

The managing editor also proofed the first two chapters, but he now suddenly finds himself busy with books two and three. He apologizes that there is no style sheet: as he always follows the same style and was expecting to proof the galleys himself, he didn't bother to prepare one. He also mentions that his copy editing job was a little rushed.

He tells you that the company has bought the rights to a great deal of artwork that was used in a more academic work by the same author. These photographs are already in film and for the most part will have to be used as they are. His final comment is that he hasn't been pleased with the typesetter's work and is expecting a bargaining session on alterations costs.

Note: The galleys for your use appear on pages 150–162, and the edited manuscript on pages 163–185.

Ex001$$$$2   TYPOSET   EnviroPub   Keep It Grren   galley 41

1   catch: chatper3

2

Acid Rain

3

Poison from the sky

4 Acid rain in Canada is a frightening story. Acid rain causes devas-
5 tating damage to our lakes, rivers, fish, ducks, trees, and to our
6 own health, and it increases year by year. But the acid rain story
7 also contains a germ of hope for the future. More than any other
8 environmental issue, it has united Canadians, particularly those in
9 Central Canada. No one argues against stopping acid rain. We all
10 are frightened of the impact that it has and are determined to do
11 something about it.
12 Canadian newspapers are regularly filled with stories about
13 acid rain. A recent article indicated that acid rain damage to sugar
14 maples in Quebec is much more serious than was previously
15 thought. An area of Quebec formally assumed to be free of acid
16 rain problems now shows half it's maple trees losing much of their
17 foliage. This loss of leaves is an early indicator of serious acid rain
18 damage. Quebec used to be called the maple-syrup capital of the
19 world; the days of that reputation may be numbered. Quebec's
20 8000 maple syrup producers estimate that they have lost up to
21 $110 million income because of acid rain.
22 It is sadly apropriate that the maple tree should be so vulner-
23 able to acid rain. The maple leaf is the official symbol of Canada. It
24 represents this land. If the maple dies, so does part of the essence
25 of Canada.
26 Everybody knows what acid rain is. Polls indicate that almost
27 all Canadians, and many Americans, know about this menace to
28 the environment. Yet as recently as the mid-1970s, the term "acid
29 rain" was virtually unknown.
30 Awareness of the problem has grown rapidly. The media regu-
31 larly report research detailing how many lakes are being killed,
32 and how trees are dying. Now new evidence links human respira-
33 tory problems to acid rain. The highly political nature of acid rain,
34 as a major conflict between Canada and the U.S., also makes it a
35 big media story.

36 **What acid rain does to our environment**

37 Like many other things that seem unfair in life, acid rain hurts the
38 most vulnerable and defenseless parts of nature first. Because of
39 prevailing wind patterns, clouds full of sulfur dioxide and
40 nitrogen oxides from central Canada and the U.S. drift northeast
41 over the most susceptible areas of the continent, where the soils
42 are thinnest and the bedrock is granite. These areas have little
43 natural limestone to counteract the acidity falling in the rain.
44 "Clean rain" has a pH count of 5.6 (the pH scale is a chemist's
45 term to refer to the acidity or alkalinity of a solution). When acid
46 rain increases acidity of lakes and rivers, the pH count goes down.
47 At a pH level of 5.0, many fish species no longer reproduce; frogs
48 and salamanders cannot survive. If a water system reaches a pH of 4.5, all fish
49 life will be dead.
50 In a recent Ontario study of 4000 lakes, 155 were almost comp-
51 letely dead; nearly 3000 showed serious acidification. A dozen
52 rivers in Nova Scotia can no longer support Atlantic salmon. U.S.
53 research suggests that over half of the lakes in the eastern states
54 receive sufficient acid rain to have significant damage.
55 To compound the problem, these geologically sensitive areas
56 also get a lot of snow. Sulphur dioxide and nitrogen oxides fall in
57 snow just as in rain. But in snow they do not enter water systems
58 immediately. Rather, the acids are stored in the accumulating
59 snow. Then in spring, just as most fish and amphibians enter their
60 spawning or reproductive periods, melting snow releases the pol-
61 lutants into the streams and lakes all at once. The massive on-
62 slaught is referred to as acid shock. Water from melting snow has
63 been found to be up to 1000 times more acidic than normal.
64 When acid rain falls on land, it gradually sinks in and makes
65 its way underground. There it can dissolve metals in the earth like
66 aluminum, mercury, cadmium and lead. The levels of these
67 poisonous metals become much higher than normal in water
68 systems. Increased levels of aluminum clog the gills of fish,
69 causing them to suffocate and die. Aluminum has also been linked
70 to Alzheimers disease in humans. Other metals that accumulate in
71 fish tissue harm the birds, animals and people who eat them.
72 Larger animals that live around water systems—ducks, loons,
73 herons, otter and mink—suffer from eating fish and other aquatic
74 life. They also gradually run out of food as the lakes and rivers
75 become too acidified to support life.
76 Not only water systems, and those creatures that live in and
77 around them, are affected by acid rain. Increasing evidence shows
78 that forests are starting to be hit too. Sugar maples in Quebec are
79 dying at an alarming rate. Beech, red maple and yellow birch in
80 New Brunswick and Nova Scotia also show signs of decline.
81 Acid rain apparently interferes with photo-synthesis in the

| Ex001$$$$2 | TYPOSET | EnviroPub | Keep | It | Grren | galley | 43 |

82 leaves of some trees. It increases the vulnerability of trees to dis-
83 ease and insects. Higher levels of acidity affect decomposition on
84 the forest floor, altering the natural cycle of growth and decay
85 which replenishes the soil feeding the trees.

86 Scientists now expect serious damage to Canada's forests in
87 the future, as trees lose their abilities to survive the effects of acid
88 rain. The forest industry in Canada employs a million people di-
89 rectly and indirectly, almost one out of every ten jobs in this
90 country. No other industry contributes as much to Canada's ba-
91 lance of payments, with $13 billion in exports annually. We are in
92 for some devastating economic impacts if predictions of forest
93 destruction from acid rain come true.

94 Acid rain also affects other parts of our society. Agriculture
95 may be hurt in some areas. In our cities, buildings are being eaten
96 away and requiring increasingly frequent repairs - estimated at
97 billions of dollars annually before long.

98 Human health is the main question mark right now. Some
99 initial research correlates heavy acid precipitation with
100 significant increases arriving of people at hospitals with
101 respiratory problems. Maybe only damage to our own health will
102 convince us that the costs of acid rain have become too high.

103 **Where acid rain comes from**

104 Our industrial/consumer lifestyle is very costly ecologically. Acid
105 rain is one of those costs.

106 Large ore smelters spew out tonnes of sulfur dioxide and nitro-
107 gen oxides from their smokestacks. Coal-burning power plants
108 pump out massive quantities of these same emissions. Oil refiner-
109 ies and other industrial facilities contribute a smaller share. The
110 cars and trucks that we drive emit nitrogen oxides into the atmo-
111 sphere.

112 These invisible gases drift through the atmosphere. There,
113 they are transformed by sunlight and moisture into sulphuric acid
114 and nitric acid. As the water vapour falls to earth in the form of
115 rain or snow, it carries with it this deadly cargo of dissolved acids.
116 By the time these chemicals reach earth as acid rain, the pollutants
117 may have travelled hundreds or thousands of kilometres from
118 their sources.

119 Though debates continue about how much damage acid rain
120 causes, no one disputes where the pollution originates. Most of the
121 Canadian sulfur dioxide comes from the huge INCO smelter at
122 Sudbury, Ontario, and the Noranda smelter in northwest Quebec.
123 Most American acid rain comes from coal-burning power plants in

| Ex001$$$$2 | TYPOSET | EnviroPub | Keep It Grren | galley 44 |

124   the Ohio Valley.

125   **INCO Comes Around—Slowly**
126   INCO's superstack at their Sudbury refinery has become an inter-
127   national symbol of acid rain. Ironically, it was built to combat air
128   pollution. The Sudbury area had suffered for years because of
129   pollution from INCO's smelter. The world's largest chimney was
130   intended to disburse the emissions beyond Sudbury. In fact, the air
131   quality around Sudbury did improve significantly after the stack
132   was completed in 1972. But though the tons of sulphur being
133   emitted from the stack no longer fell on Sudbury, they hadn't
134   disappeared. Rather, they disbursed over a wider area, remaining
135   in the atmosphere longer, allowing more of the chemicals to be
136   changed by water vapor into sulphuric acid and to fall as acid rain.

137   Sulphur dioxide has been released by INCO (and its prede-
138   cessors) in the Sudbury area since 1886. By 1916, 600,000 tonnes
139   of sulphur dioxide were being emitted each year, with an average
140   *daily* output of 1644 tonnes. Over the decades, the Sudbury smelter
141   became one of the major international sources of nickel. But the
142   price being paid for that prosperity was a staggering amount of
143   pollution. By 1960, INCO spewed on average of 6,218 tonnes of
144   sulfur dioxide into the atmosphere *every day of the year*!

145   As a society, we were slow to recognize the disasterous effects
146   of these emissions. The poor quality of Sudbury's air was the most
147   obvious problem. That was tackled by building progressively taller
148   smokestacks, to send the offending emissions farther and farther
149   afield. Both INCO and the rest of us seemed to assume that if the
150   pollution was sent high enough it would disappear and cause no
151   problem.

152   For decades, this plume of destructive fumes continued un-
153   challenged. The provincial government in Ontario did start re-
154   sponding to public concern in the late sixties. They ordered INCO
155   to reduce emissions from 5000 tonnes per day to 750 by 1978.
156   When the deadline arrived, however, INCO was still emitting over
157   3600 tonnes per day. They claimed that they could do no better.
158   The government accepted their arguments. INCO claimed to have
159   no money for pollution control. Yet at the same time they spent a
160   reported $238 million dollars in 1974 buying the largest battery
161   manufacturer in the U.S. as an investment. Protecting the enviro-
162   nment has, for most of our history been viewed as a luxury, not a
163   necessity. In this case, clearly, the environment came well below
164   profit motives.

Ex001$$$$2   TYPOSET   EnviroPub   Keep   It   Grren   galley   45

165   In 1980, public pressure pushed the government to start leaning on
166   INCO again. The province ordered INCO to reduce emissions to 2,500
167   tonnes per day immediately and to 1,950 tonnes per day by mid-1983.
168   In September of 1983, representatives of the churches met with senior
169   INCO management. Company officials frankly admitted that IN-
170   CO pollution was a major contributor to continental acid rain, but
171   argued that their financial situation prevented them from doing any-
172   thing more in the immediate future.
173   Arguments between INCO, groups concerned about the environ-
174   ment, and the government continued. Eventually the company an-
175   nounced it would reduce its emissions by the year 1994 to under 1000
176   tonnes per day. The Government of Ontario has imposed strict
177   regulations to ensure that INCO makes these reductions. Though
178   federal and provincial moneys were available, INCO decided to pay
179   for the clean-up of their emissions themselves. It will cost about $500
180   million!
181   INCO continues to be the largest single-point source of sulphur
182   dioxide emissions in North America. But cutting their emissions to
183   the 1994 target would represent a 70% reduction from 1980 levels.
184   This would make a significant contribution to Canada's goal of
185   reducing 1980 levels by 50% by 1994.

186   **Noranda demands tax dollars to clean up**
187   Noranda contrasts strikingly in corporate attitude with INCO. For
188   years, the official position of Noranda was that what goes up doesn't
189   necessarily come down. They acknowledged that their Horne Smelter
190   at Rouyn-Noranda in northwest Quebec emitted a lot of sulphur
191   dioxide. But they also steadfastly maintained that they were not a
192   significant contributor to acid rain.
193   Noranda began smelting ore from a large copper mine in the
194   area in 1923. Eventually, that ore body was exhausted. The smelter
195   now handles ore transported from distant mines. The local
196   environment around the smelter was devastated over the years by
197   the sulphur emissions. Luc Chartrand, writing in *Quebec Science*,
198   described the area as "an open wound in the northwestern ecosys-
199   tem: dead lakes, defoliated forests where even the humus has dis-
200   appeared."
201   As at INCO, the initial strategy to deal with local air pollution
202   was to build smoke stacks that would send the emissions farther
203   afield. Two stacks 160 and 140 metres high successfully decreased the
204   sulphur dioxide emissions that fell in the immediate vicinity, by
205   sending them greater distances.
206   The Horne Smelter is now the second largest single source of
207   sulphur dioxide emissions in North America. In 1965, it spewed out
208   704,000 tonnes of sulphur dioxide. For most of the '70s, annual
209   emission levels ranged between 514,000 to 608,000. In 1982, it still

Ex001$$$$2   TYPOSET   EnviroPub   Keep It Grren   galley 46

210	discharged about 555,000 tonnes.
211	Noranda has frequently added an emotionally powerful ar-
212	gument to avoid emission control programs. The company has
213	threatened to close the plant if they are forced to pay for new pol-
214	lution control technologies. The Horne Smelter is old.
215	Modernizing to reduce emissions would be expensive. And since
216	the ore that the smelter handles has to be transported into the area,
217	anyway there may be valid reasons for questioning the
218	continuation of the operation at all. But it is one of the few sources
219	of employment in an economically depressed area—so the threat
220	has plenty of clout.
221	Nevertheless, the Home Smelter produced profits of millions
222	of dollars annually for Noranda for decades. And despite their
223	threats, the company shows no plans to close it in the immediate
224	future.
225	Finally, the provincial government of Quebec decided to get
226	tough. In July 1984, they announced plans to force Noranda to
227	reduce sulphur dioxide emissions from the Horne Smelter by 50%
228	by 1989. Simultaneously, the province's environment ministry re-
229	leased a study documenting Noranda's contribution to the acid
230	rain problem in the province.
231	Complex negotiations on cost sharing occupied the next
232	couple of years. In early 1987, Noranda, and the federal and
233	provincial governments agreed to share the costs of constructing a
234	facility at Noranda to transform sulphur dioxide into sulphuric
235	acid. Acid rain-causing emissions would be reduced by 45%.
236	Canada's second largest contributor to acid rain was also
237	being brought into line—with hefty incentives of fines and of tax
238	dollars to aid their modernisation! Canada's goal of reducing its
239	emissions that create acid rain by 50% had taken another major
240	step forward.
241	With Noranda, the offer of public funds was necessary to get
242	the company to adopt major pollution reduction programmess.
243	This raises a significant question of social ethics. Is it appropriate
244	for the public to have to contribute to the clean-up costs for a
245	private company? Or should the one profiting from the pollution
246	bear the expense? A political decision was made, to be willing to
247	spend tax dollars, because of the seriousness of the problem and
248	the likelihood that it would not be dealt with without financial
249	assistance. Public opinion polls show support for those decisions.
250	But was it right?

251 Ontario Hydro embarasses Canadians

| 252 | Ontario Hydro represents a different set of problems. Here a pub- |

Ex001$$$$2   **TYPOSET**   **EnviroPub**   **Keep It Grren**   **galley 47**

253
254
255
256
257
258

lidly-owned utility is one of the major Canadian contributors to acid rain. With such anger among Canadians about acid rain, I consider it something of a scandal that a public corporation should be so negligent in controlling emissions. The Parliamentary Sub-committee on Acid Rain did not mince words in their 1983 report *Time Lost*:

259
260
261
262
263
264

> This Crown Corporation, the largest and most powerful utility in the country, situated in Canada's industrial heartland, has the responsibility to lead the way in acid rain control, to set an example for other industries to emulate. That it has not done so, but instead has forfeited its leadership role, is at best unworthy and, at worst, irresponsible. (p. 23)

265
266
267
268
269
270
271
272
273
274
275
276
277
278
279
280
281
282
283
284
285
286
287
288
289
290
291
292
293
294
295
296
297

Ontario Hydro's sources of sulphur dioxide and nitrogen oxide emissions are primarily their coal-burning electrical generating plants. Hydro operates five coal-burning power plants. In 1980, these facilities released about 452 000 t. This represents about 20% of all sulphur dioxide emissions in Ontario that year.

Hydro has constantly shifted its response to criticism about acid rain. At certain times, they have suggested converting the plants from coal to gas. At other times, they have claimed that because demand for electricity was falling, they would need to use the coal-fired plants less, thus reducing emissions anyway. At certain times, they have claimed that because demand for electricity was falling, they would need to use the coal-fired plants less, thus reducing emissions anyway. Using lower sulphur coal from Alberta could also produce fewer emissions than the high sulphur coal that hydro imported from the U.S. But their major argument has been that if they build more nuclear plants, their dependence upon the coal will diminish. For those of us who do not view nuclear power with particular enthusiasm, this strategy leaves much to be desired.

None of these approaches has been successful. Only one Toronto generating facility was converted to gas. Recently, Hydro has revised upwards their projections for electricity demand. They also claim that they cannot afford lower sulphur coal from Alberta. They say that U.S. high sulphur coal is cheaper for them. Recurring problems with the nuclear plants, that have required some extensive and expensive shut-downs for repair, resulted in even more use of coal-burning stations, and thus even higher emissions.

Ontario Hydro has always tried to avoid the most effective strategy of all for reducing emissions from coal-burning plants. Devices called scrubbers can reduce sulphur dioxide emissions by up to 90%. The process simply involves spraying limestone into the furnace, where it mixes with the sulphur dioxide, trapping it in

Ex001$$$$2   **TYPOSET**   **EnviroPub**   **Keep It Grren**   **galley 48**

298   a solid sediment.

299   Hydro estimates the cost of installing scrubbers at about $500
300   million per plant. As part of their on-again, off-again campaign
301   against installing scrubbers, Hydro has sometimes tried to scare
302   consumers by suggesting how much this expense would add to
303   their hydro bills. That approach has not generated much sympathy
304   for Ontario Hydro. Public concern about acid rain is sufficiently
305   high that people do not seem to mind the prospect of paying a bit
306   more a month if it will help.

307   Another strategy that could make a big difference—if Ontario
308   Hydro were to accept it is a central part of their mandate—is en-
309   couraging Ontario residents and industry to conserve energy. We
310   have a vast potential for energy conservation in Canada. We have
311   been slow to recognize that producing more and more energy
312   causes major environmental problems. Acid rain is only one of
313   these problems. Coal-burning plants also release a lot of carbon
314   dioxide, which contributes greatly to the global warming trend.
315   Unfor-
316   tunately, Ontario Hydro still seems to want to expand their
317   production capacity continually. Their gestures toward energy
318   conservation pale in comparison to their expansion activities.

319   Ontario governments have often appeared weak-kneed to-
320   wards Ontario Hydro, as if the utility were an empire unto itself,
321   answerable to no-one. The historic willingness of the government
322   to accept Hydro's excuses for not reducing their acid rain causing
323   emissions lends credence to that criticism.

324   But the Ontario government gradually decided to get tough
325   with Hydro. In 1981, they ordered Hydro to reduce its sulphur
326   dioxide emissions by 43% by 1990. That would bring their
327   emissions down to 260,000 tonnes annually. Four years later in
328   1985, new regulations were adopted to force Ontario Hydro to
329   reduce emissions of sulphur dioxide to 175,000 tonnes by 1994.
330   Hydro may finally have to install scrubbers or some other equally
331   effective pollution control device on their coal-burning plants. The
332   image of a public corporation having to be pushed into acting in a
333   socially responsible way has embarassed Canadians, particularly
334   Ontario residents.

335   Ontario Hydro's behavior has certainly not helped Canada's
336   case in arguing for acid rain controls south of the border. Though
337   the U.S. has many more coal-fired power plants than we do, at
338   least some have installed scrubbers. Canadians trying to put
339   pressure on the U.S. have always felt particularly vulnerable, lest
340   Ontario Hydro's record be used to undermine our position. What
341   makes it so galling is that such embarrassment should be caused
342   by a *public* utility. (In dealing with corporaions, the churches have

Ex001$$$$2   **TYPOSET**   **EnviroPub**   **Keep**   **It**   **Grren**   **galley**   **49**

343
344

found that public corporations are not necessarily more sensitive to the public mood than are private ones.)

345

Transportation receives tougher control standards

346
347
348
349
350

As well as sulphur dioxide, coal-burning electrical plants and smelters also emit some nitrogen oxides, but in much smaller quantities. We, the general public, create most of the nitrogen oxides that contribute to acid rain. They come from transportation, and about a third of the total is produced by our cars.

351
352
353
354
355
356
357

For years, Canada lagged far behind the United States in standards for auto emissions. Until the mid-1980's, Canada allowed emissions of 3.1 grams of nitrogen oxides per vehicle-mile, more than three times the U.S. standard of 1.0. (California had an even more restricted limit of 0.4.) In the early stages of our battle with the Americans over acid rain, this under cut our credibility as much as Ontario Hydro did.

358
359
360
361
362
363
364
365

The Canadian Coalition on Acid Rain and other concerned groups, including some of the churches in Canada, pressed the federal government for years to make auto standards more stringent. The government's slowness to move was always a mystery to us. Granted, a strong lobby from the petroleum industry and the car makers wanted to leave standards as they were. But the arguments of these two groups seemed weak since tougher standards were already in place in the U. S.

366
367
368
369

Ironically—perhaps pathetically—the lobby group of the petroleum industry fighting those stricter standards was called PACE, the Petroleum Association for Conservation of the Canadian Environment!

370
371
372
373
374

In any case, concern about the contribution of nitrogen oxides to acid rain eventually prevailed. The federal government announced in 1985 that new cars and light trucks in Canada would be forced to meet tougher control standards, effective September . 1987.

375

The United States resists action

376
377
378
379
380

Here, the going gets tough. Dealing with the United States has never been easy for Canadians. For most of our history, we have coexisted as friendly neighbours. But when conflicts arise, the drastic difference in population size puts Canadians at a considerable disadvantage.

381
382
383
384
385

For over a decade acid rain has been one of those conflicts. The American reaction to growing awareness of acid rain has varied from complacency to intransigence. The Canadian response has been increasing resentment and anger. The U.S. has destroyed a lot of good will this side of the border. At least half of the acid

Ex001$$$2   TYPOSET   EnviroPub   Keep   It   Grren   galley   50

386   rain falling on Canada comes from the U.S. In some areas it runs as

387   high as 70%. Wind currents carry some Canadian emissions to the

388   U.S., but no more than 10% to 15% of acid rain falling in the U.S.

389   can be blamed on Canada.

390   Most of the sulfur dioxide and nitrogen oxide emissions from

391   the U.S. originate in the coal-burning electrical generating stations

392   of the Ohio Valley. About two-thirds of the 30 million tonnes of

393   sulphur dioxide spewing out of American smoke stacks comes

394   from electrical utilities. Ironically, the oil crisis of the early 1970s

395   caused the U.S. to convert many gas-fired generating stations to

396   coal. Furthermore, much of the coal used in U.S. plants is high in

397   sulphur content.

398   Some 1979 statistics listed the 50 coal-fired power plants that

399   produced the most sulphur dioxide in eastern North America.

400   Three belonged to Ontario Hydro; the other 47 were all American.

401   Canadian plants produced 406,000 tons of sulphur dioxide that

402   year, compared with 7,515,000 tons produced in the U.S. Some

403   newer plants have had pollution control devices installed, but

404   present U.S. legislation does not require the older facilities which

405   are the main culprits to clean up their emissions.

406   Successive Canadian federal governments, and a couple of

407   provincial governments, have tried to push the U.S. to tackle acid

408   rain. Many of us think that Canada could have been much more

409   aggressive over the past few years.

410   For a while, Canada tried to blackmail the U.S., by refusing to

411   make reductions to our sources of sulphur dioxide and nitrogen

412   oxide until they improved their record. Of course, that did not

413   work. American political leaders were not particularly concerned

414   about acid rain, to or from Canada. They were much more

415   concerned about the cost, the economic dislocation that they

416   thought would be caused by tackling acid rain.

417   Canada gave up that approach in 1984, and embarcked on the

418   plan to reduce our emissions by 50 per cent by 1994. The hope was

419   that unilatoral action would shame the Americans into making a

420   comparable commitment.

421   Susceptibility to shame is not a strong American characteristic.

422   The Canadian program provided our allies in the States with extra

423   ammunition. But others, from lobbyists for the coal industry and

424   and the electrical utilities to some politicians, poked holes in

425   Canada's program. In 1986, Citizens for Sensible Control of Acid

426   Rain, a lobby group financed largely by U.S. electricity and coal

427   companies, spent $3 million U.S. fighting proposed acid rain

428   controls in Congress. No other single lobby group has spent so

429   much trying to influence U.S. legislators on any issue.

430   The official response continued to be avoidance. Until 1986,

431   former President Reagan even refused to admit that acid rain was

432   a serious environmental problem. Despite the monumental weight

Ex001$$$$2   TYPOSET   EnviroPub   Keep It Grren   galley 51

433 of scientific evidence about the damage caused by acid rain, the
434 U.S. Government maintained that more study was needed before
435 any action would be taken.
436 The Canadian churches have pushed their American coun-
437 terparts to get involved and to recognise acid rain as a major
438 stewardship issue. In January 1984, the Canadian churches
439 brought representatives of the major U.S. denominations to
440 Toronto for a three-day intensive workshop on acid rain. It paid
441 off—the Americans agreed to work with us to get U.S. action on
442 acid rain.
443 Some of the American denominations have done education
444 work with their congregations, and have encouraged their mem-
445 bers to press politicians for action on acid rain. In June of 1986,
446 I was asked to speak to an annual meeting of one of the synods of
447 the Presbyterian Church in the U.S. I found them very receptive. I
448 quite bluntly expressed Canadian frustration at the American
449 inaction on acid rain. Responses to my speech indicated that we
450 had some good allies in that room. People were embarrassed.
451 Several speakers vowed to push their churches and their govern-
452 ments to take the problem much more seriously.
453 George Bush had always defended the Reagan administra-
454 tion's denial of scientific evidence linking acid rain to ecological
455 damage. However, he discovered the environment during his 1988
456 election campaign. Suddenly, Bush was vowing that a Bush
457 administration would take decisive action on acid rain. There are
458 also some encouraging signs from Congress.
459 Whether real action happens will depend on how convinced
460 Americans become that acid rain hurts them. In the meantime,
461 American acid rain continues to fall on Canada unabated.

462 ## What Can We Do

463 ### Learn More About Acid Rain
464 There are some excellent sources of up-to-date information on
465 the affects of acid rain, what is being done about it, and what
466 needs to be done. The Canadian Coalition on Acid Rain brings
467 together many different organizations, including environmental
468 groups, labor unions, tourist associations, organizations of native
469 peoples, and churches. It is the largest environmental coalition in
470 Canada, a testimony to the seriousness with which people in many
471 different parts of Canadian society view the acid rain problem.
472 Joining the Coalition will give you access to reliable, detailed
473 information, and will link you into a network that suggests specific
474 actions for lobbying against acid rain.
475 Groups might show a very good film produced by the
476 National Film Board of Canada, entitled *Acid Rain: Requiem or
477 Recovery*. Several years ago, the American administration banned
478 distribution of this movie in the U.S., on the grounds that it was

| Ex001$$$$2 | TYPOSET | EnviroPub | Keep It Grren | galley 52 |

479 propaganda. The film runs about half an hour, and gives a concise
480 overview of what causes acid rain and how it affects our
481 ecosystem. It is available in all regional outlets of the National Film
482 Board, and from some libraries.
483 Environment Canada has produced some helpful information,
484 as have the provincial governments, particularly Ontario and
485 Quebec. Writing to them directly or through your MP or MLA will
486 get you a lot of literature.

487 **Monitor Canadian governments and polluters The federal**
488 **government and governments in provinces that produce acid**
489 **rain have all passed regulations to significantly reduce the**
490 **emissions coming from polluting industries and utilities. But**
491 **passing regulations and enforcing regulations are quite different**
492 **matters. The Auditor-General in Ontario recently criticized the**
493 **province's Department   of the Environment for rallying too**
494 **greatly on data from the polluting industries themselves to**
495 **monitor compliance with the regulations.**
496 As the result of public pressure, politicians in Canada have
497 taken some significant steps to adress the acid rain problem. But
498 that pressure has to be kept up. The federal government slipped in
499 its commitment in early 1988 by taking a very weak position on
500 nitrogen oxide emissions during a meeting of 30 countries in
501 Europe. Like industries, governments need to be constantly
502 monitored. Otherwise, they may assume that Canadians no longer
503 care about acid rain. Writing to your MP and MLA keeps them
504 aware of your concern.
505 The companies contributing to acid rain in Canada are mainly
506 in Ontario, Quebec and the Maritime provinces. They too are sen-
507 sitive to public opinion. Write and express your concern about
508 acid rain and ask them for information on how they intend to
509 comply with the regulations. They must be kept accountable.

510 **Educate the United States**

511 Canadian problems and Candian news have little impact on
512 our somewhat insular neighbors. Our politicians must do a better
513 job of educating decision makers in Washington and state capitols.
514 The federal goverment has to be pressured about their action
515 9or lack of it0 in getting the United States to introduce legislation
516 which will reduce acid rain-causing omissions. The Americans are
517 our biggest problem.
518 Prime Minister Mulroney liked to think that he could persuade
519 President Reagan to take action because of the "special
520 relationship" between the two leaders. In retrospect, it seems
521 Reagan used that "special relationship" to delude Mulroney.
522 Canadians have to communicate clearly and forcefully to our
523 MP's, the Prime Minister, the Minister of the Environment, and the

Ex001$$$$2   TYPOSET   EnviroPub   Keep It Grren   galley 53

524
525   Minister of External Affairs that we consider acid rain serious
526   enough to set aside the usual niceties of diplomatic relations with
       our big neighbor to the south, and to adopt a much tougher stand.
527   The federal government could do more aggressively lobby of
528   the U.S. Administration and Congress. They could initiate more
529   public education in the U.S. to convince Americans that acid rain
530   control is in their bast interests too.
531   There is also the   possibility of legal action. Already, the
532   Ontario   Government   has   participated   with   several
533   northeastern States to try and force the U.S. Environmental
534   Protection Agency to act on acid rain. The federal government
535   could attempt this route as well.
536   American politicians are not elected by Canadian voters, so
537   they may pay little attention to us. Nevertheless, writing to them
538   and letting them know how angry Canadians are getting about
539   U.S. inaction, cannot hurt. Many Americans have personal and
540   and business connections with Canada. Communication could
541   increase the pressure to ensure that we remain good neighbours.
542   We could do some personal education and lobbying with
543   American citizens. Many Canadians travel to the US for
544   business and vacations. Many Americans come to Canada for the
545   same reasons. Such visits give us an opportunity to let Americans
546   know personally how upset we are about *their* pollution killing our
547   environment. Many Americans don't yet understand the
548   seriousness of the problem. They might then be more prepared to
549   pressure their politicians back home to take acid rain seriously.
550   In some ways, arid rain tests our concern about the future of
551   the earth. The issue has gotten lots of publicity.
552   Canadians can't claim that they don't know what it's about.
553   The results are clearly documented in a great deal of scientific
554   research.
555   If we are not concerned about acid rain, than we probably
556   won't care about any of the other threats to creation. Acid rain is
557   an issue that demands a response.

558   ## Resources for further information

559   *The Canadian Coalition on Acid Rain*, 112 St. Clair Ave. W., Suite 504,
560   Toronto, ON, M4V 2Y3 (416) 968-2135

561   *The Canadian Environmental Network*, 1289 Station B, Ottawa, ON, K1P
562   5R3 (613) 563-2078

563   Pollution Probe, Ecology House, 12 Madison Ave., Toronto, ON M5R 2S1.
564   (416) 926-1907.

565   *A Killing Rain*—The Global Threat of Acid Precipitation, by T. Pawlick,
566   Douglas & Macintyre, 1984.

567   *The Acid Rain Primer*, 4th edition 1988, Pollution Probe, 12 Madison Ave.,
568   Toronto, ON M5R 2S1. Tel. 926-1907.

catch:
Chapter 3

(CH)   Acid Rain
(CSH) Poison from the Sky

Acid rain in Canada is a frightening story. Acid rain
causes devastating damage to our lakes, rivers, fish,
ducks, trees, and to our own health, and it increases
year by year. But the acid rain story also contains a
germ of hope for the future. More than any other
environmental issue, it has united Canadians,
particularly those in central Canada. No one argues
against stopping acid rain. We all are frightened of the
impact that it has and are determined to do something
about it.

Canadian newspapers are regularly filled with stories
about acid rain. A recent article indicated that acid
rain damage to sugar maples in Quebec is much more
serious than was previously thought. An area of Quebec
formerly assumed to be free of acid rain problems now
shows half its maple trees losing much of their foliage. This
loss of leaves is an early indicator of serious acid
rain damage. Quebec used to be called the maple syrup   (stet)
capital of the world; the days of that reputation may be
numbered. Quebec's eight thousand 8,000 maple syrup producers
estimate that they have lost up to $110 million dollars
in income because of acid rain.

It is sadly apropriate that the maple tree should be
so vulnerable to acid rain. The mapleleaf is, as well as
an economic asset, the official symbol of Canada. It
represents this land. If the maple dies, so does part of
the essence of Canada.

Everybody knows what acid rain is, and polls indicate
that almost all Canadians, and many Americans, know about
this menace to the environment. Yet as recently as the
mid-1970s, the term "acid rain" was virtually unknown.

Awareness of the problem has grown rapidly. The media
regularly reports research detailing how many lakes are
being killed, and how trees are dying. Now new evidence
links human respiratory problems to acid rain. The
highly political nature of acid rain, as a major area of
conflict between Canada and the U.S., also makes it a big
media story.

(A)→ What acid rain does to our environment

Like many other things that seem unfair in life, acid
rain hurts the most vulnerable and defenseless parts of
nature first. Because of prevailing wind patterns,
clouds full of sulfur dioxide and nitrogen oxides form
central Canada and the U.S. drift north east over the
most susceptible areas of the continent, where the soils
are thinnest and the bedrock is granite. These areas
have little natural lime stone to counteract the acidity
falling in the rain.

"Clean rain" has a pH count of 5.6 (the pH scale is a
chemist's term to refer to the acidity or alkalinity of a
solution). When acid rain increases acidity of lakes and
rivers, the pH count goes down. At a pH level of 5.0 many
fish species no longer reproduce; frogs and salamanders
cannot survive. If a water system reaches a pH of 4.5, all
fish life will be dead have died.

In a recent Ontario study of 4000 lakes, 155 were
almost completely dead; nearly 3000 showed serious
acidification. A dozen Nova Scotian rivers can no longer
support Atlantic salmon. U.S. research suggests that

over half of the lakes in the eastern States receive
sufficient acid rain to have significant damage.

To compound the problem, these geologically sensitive
areas also get a lot of snow. Sulphur dioxide and
nitrogen oxides fall in snow as ~~just like they also fall~~ in
rain. But in snow they do not enter water systems
immediately. ~~In snow, on the other hand,~~ Rather, the acids are
stored in the accumulating snow. Then in spring, just as
most fish and amphibians enter their spawning or
reproductive periods, melting snow releases the
pollutants into the streams and lakes all at once. The
massive onslaught is referred to as acid shock. Water
from melting snow has been found to be up to 100 times
more acidic than normal.

When acid rain falls on land, it gradually sinks in
and makes its way underground. There it can dissolve
metals in the earth like aluminum, mercury, cadmium, and
lead. The levels of these poisonous metals become much
higher than normal in water systems. Increased levels of
aluminum clog the gills of fish, causing them to
suffocate and die. Aluminum has also been linked to
Alzheimer's disease in humans. Other metals that
accumulate in fish tissue harm the birds, animals and
people who eat them.

Larger animals that live around water systems, ducks,
loons, herons, otter, and mink, suffer from eating fish
and other aquatic life. They also gradually run out ~~short~~ of
food ~~until finally none is left~~ as the lakes and rivers
become too acidified to support life.

Not only water systems, and those creatures that live
in and around them, are affected by acid rain.
Increasing evidence shows ~~indicates~~ that forests are starting ~~beginning~~

to ~~feel the brunt~~ be hit too. Sugar maples in Quebec are dying
at an alarming rate. Beech, red maple and yellow birch
in New Brunswick and Nova Scotia also show signs of
decline.

Acid rain apparently ~~seriously~~ interferes with photo-
synthesis in the leaves of some trees. It increases the
vulnerability of trees to disease and insects. Higher
levels of acidity affect decomposition on the forest
floor, altering the natural cycle of growth and decay
which replenishes the soil feeding the trees.

Scientists now expect serious damage to Canada's
forests in the future, as trees lose their abilities to
survive the effects of acid rain. The forest industry in
Canada employs a million people directly and indirectly,
almost one out of every ten jobs in this country. No
other industry contributes as much to Canada's balance
of payments, with $13 billion ~~dollars~~ in exports
annually. We are in for some devastating economic
impacts if predictions of forest destruction from acid
rain come true.

Acid rain also effects other parts of our society.
Agriculture may be hurt in some areas. In our cities,
buildings are ~~getting~~ being eaten away and requiring
increasingly frequent repairs - estimated at billions of
dollars annually before long.

Human health is the main question mark right now. Some
initial research correlates heavy acid precipitation
with significant increases (arriving at hospitals of people) ~~having~~ with
respiratory problems. Maybe only damage to our own
health will convince us that the costs of acid rain have
become too high.

95

100

105

110

115

120

(A) Where Acid Rain Comes From

Our industrial/consumer lifestyle is very costly ecologically. Acid rain is one of those costs.

Large ore smelters spew out tonnes of sulfur dioxide and nitrogen oxides from their smokestacks. Coal-burning power plants pump out massive quantities of these same emissions. Oil refineries and other industrial facilities contribute a smaller share. The cars and trucks that we drive emit nitrogen oxides into the atmosphere.

These invisible gases drift ~~without being seen~~ through the atmosphere. There, they are transformed by sunlight and moisture into sulphuric acid and nitric acid. As the water vapour falls to earth in the form of rain or snow, it carries with it this deadly cargo of dissolved acids. By the time these chemicals reach earth as acid rain, the pollutants may have travelled hundreds or thousands of STET kilometres from their sources.

Though debates continue about how much damage acid rain causes, no one disputes where the pollution originates. Most of the Canadian sulfur dioxide comes from the huge INCO smelter at Sudbury, Ontario, and the Noranda smelter ~~that is found~~ in northwest Quebec. Most American acid rain comes from coal-burning power plants in the Ohio Valley.

(B) INCO Comes Around - Slowly

155 INCO's superstack at their Sudbury refinery has become an international symbol of acid rain. Ironically, it was built to combat air pollution. The Sudbury area had suffered for years because of pollution from INCO's smelter. The world's largest chimney was intended to
160 disburse the emissions beyond Sudbury. In fact, the air quality around Sudbury did improve significantly after the stack was completed in 1972. But though the tons of sulphur being emitted from the stack no longer fell on Sudbury, they hadn't disappeared. Rather, they disbursed
165 over a wider area, remaining in the atmosphere longer, allowing more of the chemicals to be changed by water vapor into sulphuric acid and to fall as acid rain.

Sulphur dioxide has been released by INCO (and its predecessors) in the Sudbury area since 1886. By 1916,
170 600,000 tonnes of sulphur dioxide were being emitted each year, with an average _daily_ output of 1644 tonnes. Over the decades, the Sudbury smelter became one of the major international sources of nickel. But the price tag being paid for that prosperity was a staggering amount
175 of pollution in the air. By 1960, INCO spewed on average 6,218 tonnes of sulfur dioxide into the atmosphere _every day of the year!_

As a society, we were slow to recognize the disastrous effects of these emissions. The poor quality of
180 Sudbury's air was the most obvious problem. That was tackled by building progressively taller smokestacks, to send the offending emissions farther and farther afield. Both INCO and the rest of us seemed to assume that if

the pollution was sent high enough it would ~~go away~~ disappear
~~forever and therefore there would be~~ and cause ~~no problem,~~ no problem.

For decades, this plume of destructive fumes continued
unchallenged. The provincial government in Ontario did
start responding to public concern in the late sixties.
They ordered INCO to reduce ~~its~~ emissions from 5000
tonnes per day to 750 by 1978. When the deadline
arrived, however, INCO was still emitting over 3,600
tonnes per day. They claimed that they could do no
better. The government accepted their arguments. INCO
claimed to have no money for pollution control. Yet at
the same time they spent a reported $238 million ~~dollars~~
in 1974 buying the largest battery manufacturer in the
U.S. as an investment. Protecting the environment has,
for most of our history, been viewed as a luxury, not a
necessity. In this case, clearly, the environment came
well below profit motives.

In 1980, public pressure pushed the government to
start leaning on INCO again. The province ordered INCO
to reduce emissions to 2,500 tonnes per day immediately
and to 1,950 tonnes per day by mid-1983. In September of
1983, representatives of the Churches met with senior
INCO management. Company officials frankly admitted that
INCO ~~pollutants were~~ pollution was a major contributor to continental
acid rain, but argued that their financial situation
prevented them from doing anything more in the immediate
future.

Arguments between INCO, groups concerned about the
environment, and the government continued. Eventually
the company announced it would reduce its emissions by
the year 1994 to under 1000 tonnes per day. The
Government of Ontario has imposed strict regulations to

ensure that INCO makes these reductions. Though federal
and provincial money ~s were available, INCO decided to pay
for the clean-up of their emissions themselves. It will
cost about $500 million!

220   INCO continues to be the largest single-point source
of sulphur dioxide emissions in North America. But
cutting their emissions to the 1994 target would
represent a 70% reduction from 1980 levels. This would
make a significant contribution to Canada's goal of
225 reducing (by 1994) the 1980 levels by 50%.

(B)   Noranda Demands Tax Dollars to Clean Up
   Noranda contrasts strikingly in corporate attitude
with INCO. For years, the official position of Noranda
was that what goes up doesn't necessarily come down.
230 They acknowledged that their Horne Smelter at Rouyn-
Noranda in northwest Québec emmitted a lot of sulphur
dioxides. But in stark contrast they also always stead/
fastly maintained that they were not a significant
contributor to acid rain.

235   Noranda began smelting ore from a large copper mine
in the area in 1923. Eventually, that ore body was
exhausted. The smelter now handles ore transported from
distant mines. The local environment around the smelter
was devastated over the years by the sulphur emissions.
240 Luc Chartrand, writing in Québec Science, described the
area as "an open wound in the northwestern ecosystem:
dead lakes, defoliated forests where even the humus has
disappeared."
   As at INCO, the initial strategy to deal with local air
245 pollution in its own locality was to build smoke stacks
that would send the emissions farther afield. Two stacks

160 and 140 metres high succesfully decreased the
sulphur dioxide emissions that fell in the immediate
vicinity, by sending them greater distances.

250   The Horne Smelter is now the second-largest single
source of sulphur dioxide emissions in North America. In
1965, it spewed out 704,000 tonnes of sulphur dioxide.
For most of the '70s, annual emission levels ranged
between 514,000 to 608,000. In 1982, it still discharged
255 about 555,000 tonnes.

   Noranda has frequently added an emotionally powerful
argument to avoid emission control programmes. The company has
threatened to close the plant if they are forced to pay
for new pollution control technologies. The Horne
260 Smelter is old. Modernizing to reduce emissions would be
expensive. And anyway, since the ore that the smelter
handles has to be transported into the area, there may
be valid reasons for questioning the continuation of the
operation at all. But it is one of the few sources of
265 employment in an economically depressed area - so the
threat has plenty of clout.

   Nevertheless, the Horne Smelter produced profits of millions
of dollars annually for Noranda for decades. And despite
their threats, the company shows no plans to close it in
270 the immediate future.

   Finally, the provincial government of Quebec decided
to get tough. In July 1984, they announced plans to force
Noranda to reduce sulphur
dioxide emissions from the Horne Smelter by 50% by 1989.
275 Simultaneously, the province's Ministry of the Environment
released a study documenting Noranda's contribution to
the acid rain problem in the province.

Complex negotiations on cost sharing occupied the next
couple of years. In early 1987, Noranda, and the federal
government and the provincial governments agreed to share
the costs of constructing a facility at Noranda to
transform sulphur dioxide into sulphuric acid. Acid
rain-causing emissions would be reduced by 45%.

Canada's second-largest contributor to acid rain was
also being brought into line, with hefty incentives of
fines and using of tax dollars to aid their modernisation!
Canada's goal of reducing its emissions that create acid
rain by 50% had taken another major step forward.

With Noranda, the offer of public funds was necessary
to get the company to adopt major pollution reduction
programmes. This raises a significant question of social
ethics. Is it appropriate for the public to have to
contribute to the clean-up costs for a private company?
Or should the one profiting from the pollution bear the
expense? A political decision was made, to be willing to
spend tax dollars, because of the seriousness of the
problem and the likelihood that it would not be dealt
with without financial assistance. Public opinion polls
show support for those decisions. But was it right?

Ⓑ Ontario Hydro Embarrasses Canadians

Ontario Hydro represents a different set of problems.
Here a publicly-owned utility is one of the major
Canadian contributors to acid rain. With such anger
among Canadians about the importance of the issue of
acid rain, I consider it something of a sandal that a   stet
public corpation should be so negligent in controlling

Author: Maybe "we" or another more impersonal form? — ed   No!

emissions. The Parliamentary Sub-committee on Acid Rain did not mince words in their 1983 report, _Time Lost:_ *(italic)*

310 *(9)* This Crown Corporation, the largest and most powerful utility in the country, situated in Canada's industrial heartland, has the responsibility to lead the way in in acid rain control, to set an example for other industries to emulate. That it has not done so, but instead has forfeited its leadership role, is at best 315 unworthy and, at worst, irresponsible. (p.23)

Author: page ref?

Ontario Hydro's sources of sulphur dioxide and nitrogen oxide emissions are primarily their coal-burning electrical generating plants. Hydro operates ~~8~~ five coal-burning power plants. In 1980, these facilities 320 released about 452 000 t. This represents about 20% of all sulphur dioxide emissions in Ontario that year.

Hydro has constantly shifted ~~their~~ its response to criticism about acid rain. At certain times, they have suggested converting the plants from coal to gas. At 325 other times, ~~it has~~ they have claimed that because demand for electricity was falling, they would need to use the less coal-fired plants, thus reducing emissions anyway. Using lower sulphur coal from Alberta could also produce fewer emissions than the high sulphur coal that hydro imported 330 from the U.S. But their major argument has been that if they build more nuclear plants, their dependence upon the coal will diminish. For those of us who do not view nuclear power with particular enthusiasm, this strategy leaves much to be desired.

335 None of these approaches has been ~~particularly~~ successful. Only one Toronto generating facility was

converted to gas. Recently, Hydro has revised upwards
their projections for electricity demand. They also
claim that they cannot afford lower sulphur coal from
340 Alberta. They say that U.S. high sulphur coal is cheaper
for them. Recurring problems with the nuclear plants,
that have required some extensive and expensive shut-
downs for repair, resulted in even more use of coal-
burning stations, and thus even higher emissions.

345 Ontario Hydro has always tried to avoid the most
effective strategy of all for reducing emissions from
coalburning plants. Devices called scrubbers can reduce
sulphur dioxide emissions by up to 90%. The process
simply involes spraying limestone into the furnace,
350 where it mixes with the sulphur dioxide, resulting in
the limestone trapping it in a solid sediment.

Hydro estimates the cost of installing scrubbers at
about $500 million dollars per plant. Hydro's approach
has not generated much sympathy for Ontario Hydro. As
355 part of their on-again, off-again campaign against
installing scrubbers, Hydro has sometimes tried to scare
consumers by suggesting how much this expense would add
to their hydro bills. Public concern about acid rain is
sufficiently high that people do not seem to mind the
360 prospect of paying a bit more a month if it will help.

Another strategy that could make a big difference if
Ontario Hydro were to accept it is a central part of
their mandate - is that it might convince the people who
live in Ontario and the industries that operate in
365 Ontario not to waste so much energy - in fact, to
conserve energy. We have a vast potential for energy
conservation in Canada. We have been slow to recognize
that producing more and more energy causes major

environmental problems. Acid rain is only one of these

370 problems. Coal-burning plants also release a lot of carbon dioxide, which contributes greatly to the global warming trend. Unfortunately, Ontario Hydro still seems to want to continually expand their production capacity. Their gestures toward energy conservation pale

375 in comparison to their expansion activities.

   Ontario governments have often appeared weak-kneed towards Ontario Hydro, as if the utility were an empire unto itself, answerable to no-one. The historic willingness of the government to accept Hydro's excuses

380 for not reducing their acid rain causing emissions lends credence to that criticism.

   But the Ontario government gradually decided to get tougher with Hydro. In 1981, they ordered Hydro to reduce its sulphur dioxide emissions by 43% by 1990.

385 That would bring their emissions down to 260,000 tonnes annually. Four years later, in 1985, stet adopted to force Ontario Hydro to reduce emissions of sulphur dioxide to 175,000 tonnes by 1994. Hydro may finally have to install scrubbers or

390 some other equally effective pollution control device on their coal-burning plants. The image of a public corporation having to be pushed into acting in a socially responsible way has embarrassed Canadians, particularly Ontario residents.

395   Ontario Hydro's behavior has certainly not helped Canada's case in arguing for acid rain controls south of the border. Though the U.S. has many more coal-fired power plants than we do, at least some have installed scrubbers. Canadians whereas trying to put pressure on the U.S.

400 have always felt particularly vulnerable, lest Ontario

Hydro's record be used to undermine ~~their~~ ~~our~~ position. What STET
makes it so galling is ~~when~~ that such embarrassment ~~is~~ should be caused
by a <u>public</u> utility. (In dealing with corporations, the
Churches have found that public corporations are not
necessarily more sensitive to the public mood than are
private ones.)

(B) Transportation Receives Tougher Control standards
As well as sulphur dioxide, coal-burning electrical
plants and smelters also emit some nitrogen oxides, but
in much smaller quantities. We, the general public,
create most of the nitrogen oxides that contribute to
acid rain. They come from transportation, and about a
third of the total is produced by our cars.

For years, Canada lagged far behind the United States
in standards for auto emissions. Until the mid-1980's,
Canada allowed emissions of 3.1 grams of nitrogen oxides
per vehicle-mile, more than three times the U.S.
standard of 1.0 (California had an even more restricted
limit of 0.4.) In the early stages of our battle with
the Americans over acid rain, this under cut our
credibility as much as Ontario Hydro did.

The Canadian Coalition on Acid Rain and other
concerned groups, including some of the Churches in
Canada, pressed the federal government for years to make
auto standards more stringent. The government's slowness
to move was always a mystery to ~~every thinking Canadian.~~ us. [Auth: Ok?]
Granted, a strong lobby from the petroleum industry and
the car makers wanted to leave standards as they were.
But the arguments of these two groups seemed weak since
tougher standards were already in place in the U.S.

Auth: metric equivalent?
No — TOO COMPLICATED.

Ironically ⌐ perhaps pathetically ⌐ the lobby group of
the petroleum industry fighting those stricter standards
was called PACE, the Petroleum Association for
Conservation of the Canadian Environment!

435   In any case, concern about the contribution of
nitrogen oxides to acid rain eventually prevailed. The
federal government announced in 1985 that new car and
light trucks in Canada would be forced to meet tougher
control standards, effective September 1987.

440 The United States Resists Action   lc

   Here, the going gets tough. Dealing with the United
States has never been easy for Canadians. For most of
our history, we have coexisted as friendly neighbours.
But when conflicts arose, the drastic difference in
445 population size puts Canadians at a considerable
disadvantage.

   For over a decade acid rain has been one of those
conflicts. The American reaction to growing awareness of
acid rain has varied from complacency to intransigence.
450 The Canadian response has been increasing resentment and
anger. The U.S. has destroyed a lot of goodwill this
side of the border.

   At least half of the acid rain falling on Canada comes
from the U.S. In some areas it runs as high as 70%. Wind
455 currents carry some Canadian emissions to the U.S., but
~~all Canadians and many Americans realize that~~ no more
than ~~between~~ 10% to 15% of acid rain falling in the U.S.
can be blamed on Canada.

   Most of the sulfur dioxide and nitrogen oxide
460 emissions from the U.S. originate in the coal-burning
electrical generating stations of the Ohio Valley. About

two-thirds of the 30 million tonnes of sulphur dioxide
spewing out of American smoke stacks comes from
electrical utilities. Ironically, the oil crisis ^of the early 1970s^ caused
the U.S. to convert many gas-fired generating stations
to coal. Furthermore, much of the coal used in U.S.
plants is high in sulphur content ~~, as it comes from~~
~~(West Virginia??)~~

Some 1979 sta~~t~~istics listed the ~~top~~ 50 ~~sulphur~~
~~dioxide producing~~ coal-fired power plants ^that produced the most sulphur dioxide^ in eastern
North America. Three belonged to Ontario Hydro; the
other 47 were all American. Canadian plan~~t~~s produced
406,000 tons of sulphur dioxide that year, compared with
7,515,000 tons produced in the U.S. some new~~ents~~ ^er plants^ have
had pollution control devices install~~ed~~ but present U.S.
legislation does not require the older facilities which
are the main culprits to clean up their emissions.

Successive Canadian federal governments, ~~and a couple~~ (STET)
~~of provincial governments,~~ have tried to push the U.S.
to tackle ~~aid~~ ^c^ rain. Many of us think that Canada could
have been much more aggressive over the past few years.

For a while, Canada tried to blackmail the U.S., by
refusing to make reductions to our sources of sulphur
dioxide and nitrogen oxide until they improved their
record. Of course, that did not work. American political
leaders were not particularily concerned about acid
rain, to or from Canada. The~~y~~ were ~~many~~ ^much^ more concern~~ed~~
about the cost ~~that could be incurred~~ the economic
dislocation that they thought would be caused by
tackling acid rain.

Canada ~~followed that path until~~ ^gave up that approach in^ 1984 ~~, but then stopped,~~
and ~~tried a new~~ ^embarked on the^ plan to reduce our emissions by 50 per
cent by 1994. The hope was that ~~if we acted on our own~~ ^unilateral action^

Auth:
Ok?
YES

~~to deal with the problem~~ would shame the Americans into making a comparable commitment.

Susceptibility to shame is not a strong American characteristic. The Canadian programme provided our allies in the States with extra ammunition. But others, from lobbyists for the coal industry and the electrical utilities to some politicians, poked holes in Canada's programme. In 1986, Citizens for Sensible Control of Acid Rain, a lobby group financed largely by U.S. electricity and coal companies, spent ~~three~~ 3 million ~~dollars~~ U.S. fighting proposed acid rain controls in Congress. No other single lobby group has spent so much trying to influence U.S. legislators on any issue.

The official response continued to be avoidance. Until 1986, former President Reagan even refused to admit that acid rain was a serious environmental problem ~~(vide "killer trees")~~. Despite the monumental weight of scientific evidence about the damage caused by acid rain, the U.S. Government maintained that more study was needed before any action would be taken.

The Canadian churches have pushed their American counterparts to get involved and to ~~acknowledge~~ recognize acid rain as a major stewardship issue. In January, 1984, the Canadian churches brought representatives of the major U.S. denominations to Toronto for a three-day intensive workshop on acid rain. It paid off; the Americans agreed to work with us to get U.S. action on acid rain.

Some of the American denominations have done education work with their congregations, and have encouraged their members to press politicians for action on acid rain. In June of 1986, I was asked to speak to an annual meeting of one of the Synods of the Presbyterian Church in the

U.S. I found them very receptive. I quite bluntly expressed Canadian frustration at the American inaction on acid rain. Responses to my speech indicated that we had some good allies in that room. People were embarrassed. Several speakers vowed to push their churches and their governments to take the problem much more seriously.

George Bush had always defended the Reagan administration's ~~refusal to believe~~ denial of the scientific evidence linking acid rain to ecological damage. However, he discovered the environment during his 1988 election campaign. Suddenly, Bush was vowing that a Bush administration would take decisive action on acid rain. There are also some encouraging signs from Congress. ( )

Whether real action happens will depend on how convinced Americans become that acid rain hurts them. In the meantime, American acid rain continues to fall on Canada unabated.

(A) What We Can Do

(B) Learn More About Acid Rain

There are some excellent sources of up-to-date information on the effects of acid rain, what is being done about it, and what needs to be done. The Canadian Coalition on Acid Rain brings together many different organizations, including environmental groups, labor unions, tourist associations, organizations of Native Peoples, and churches. It is the largest environmental coalition in Canada, a testimony to ~~and its very size is evidence of~~ the seriousness with which people in many different

555 parts of Canadian society view the acid rain problem. Joining the Coalition will ~~get~~ give you access to reliable, detailed information, and will link you into a network that suggests specific actions for lobbying against acid rain.

560 Groups might show a very good film produced by the National Film Board of Canada, entitled Acid Rain: Requiem or Recovery. Several ~~(eleven?)~~ years ago, the American Administration banned distribution of this movie in the U.S., on the grounds that it was 565 propaganda. The film runs about ~~one~~ half an hour, ~~is~~ ~~excellent~~ and gives a concise overview of what causes acid rain and how it affects our ecosystem. It is available in all regional outlets of the National Film Board, ~~or~~ and from some libraries.

570 Environment Canada has produced some helpful information, as have the provincial governments, particularly ~~that of~~ Ontario and Quebec. Writing to them directly or through your MP or MLA will ~~get~~ provide you a lot of ~~good~~ literature.

575 **B** Monitor Canadian Governments, and Polluters, ~~and Regulations~~ The federal government and governments in provinces that produce acid rain have all passed regulations to significantly reduce the emissions coming from polluting industries and utilites. But passing regulations and 580 enforcing regulations are quite different matters. The Auditor-General in Ontario recently criticized the province's Department of the Environment for relying too greatly on data from the polluting industries themselves to monitor compliance with the regulations.

585 As the result of public pressure, politicians in
Canada have taken some significant steps to address the
acid rain problem. But that pressure has to be kept up.
The federal government slipped in its commitment in
early 1988 by taking a very weak position on nitrogen
590 oxide emissions during a meeting of 30 countries in
Europe. Like industries, governments need to be
constantly monitored. Writing to your MP and MLA and keeps
them him or her aware of your concern. Otherwise, they may (tr)
assume that Canadians no longer care about acid rain.

595 The companies contributing to acid rain in Canada
mainly are in Ontario, Quebec, and the Maritime
provinces. They too are sensitive to public opinion.
Write and express your concern about acid rain and ask
them for information on how they intend to comply with
600 the regulations. They must be kept accountable.

(B) Educate the United States

Canadian problems and Canadian news has little impact
somewhat
on our insular neighbors south of the border. Our
politicians must do a better job of educating decision
605 makers in Washington and state capitols.
Insert
to
next
page
The federal government could do more aggressive
lobbying of the U.S. Administration and Congress. They
could initiate more pubic education in the U.S. to
convince Americans that acid rain control is in their
610 best interests too.
The federal government also has to be pressured about
their action (or lack of it) in getting the United States
to introduce legislation which will reduce acid rain-
causing emissions. The Americans are our biggest problem.

615 Prime Minister Mulroney liked to think that he could
persuade President Reagan to take action because of the
"special relationship" between the two leaders. In
retrospect, it seems Reagan used that "special
relationship" to ~~dilute~~ delude Mulroney. Canadians have to

620 communicate clearly and forcefully to our MP's, the
Prime Minister, the Minister of the Environment, and the
Minister of External Affairs that we consider acid rain
serious enough to set aside the usual niceties of
diplomatic relations with our big neighbor to the south,

625 and to adopt a much tougher stand.

Insert from previous page There is also the possibility of legal action. Already,
the Ontario Government ~~collaborating~~ has participated with several
northeastern States to try and force the U.S.
Environmental Protection Agency to act on acid rain. The

630 federal government could attempt this route as well.

American politicians are not elected by Canadian
voters, so they ~~evidently~~ may pay little attention to us.
Nevertheless, writing to them, and letting them know how
angry Canadians are getting about U.S. inaction, cannot

635 hurt. Many Americans have ~~relatives here~~ personal and and business
connections with Canada. Communication could increase
the pressure to ensure that we remain good neighbors.

We could do some personal education and lobbying with
American citizens. Many Canadians travel ~~there~~ to the US for

640 business and vacation s. ~~purposes.~~ Many Americans come to
Canada for the same reasons. Such visits give us an
opportunity to let Americans know personally how upset
we are about their pollution killing our environment. ~~I~~
Many ~~am willing to bet that~~ Americans don't yet understand

645 the seriousness of the problem. They might then be more

prepared to pressure their politicians back home to take
acid rain seriously.

650 ~~One of my friends carries a sign in his car that says "STOP ACID RAIN." Whenever he passes a car with American license plates, he flashes the sign at them. Their discomfort shows on their faces. That's a step in the right direction.~~

In some ways, acid rain tests our concern about the future
655 of the earth. The issue has gotten lots of publicity.
Canadians can't claim that they don't know what it's
about. The results are clearly documented in a great
deal of scientific research

If we are not concerned about acid rain, then we
probably won't care about any of the other threats to
660 creation. Acid rain is an issue that demands a response.
~~from us.~~

AUTH: your friend is creating
acid rain by driving his car! —ed

CUT IF YOU INSIST, BUT
IT'S A GOOD STORY

(A) Resources for further information

(ORDER)

(2) The Canadian Environmental Network, 1289 Station B,
Ottawa, ON, K1P 5R3 (613) 563-2078

(No italic)

665 (3) Pollution Probe, Ecology House, 12 Madison Ave.,
Toronto, ON M5R 2S1. (416) 926-1907.

(1) The Canadian Coalition on Acid Rain, 112 St. Clair Ave.
W., Suite 504, Toronto, ON, M4V 2Y3. (416) 968-2135

A Killing Rain - The Global Threat of Acid
670 Precipitation, by T. Pawlick, Douglas & Macintyre Publ.,
1984.

The Acid Rain Primer, 4th edition 1988, Pollution Probe,
12 Madison Ave., Toronto, ON M5R 2S1. Tel. 926-1907.

Ex Tenebris Lux

Accustomed to the plodding pace of your workplace and its mountains of hand-typed documents, you peek out of your Kremlin office one morning only to have thrust at you a thin folder that you hadn't expected to see for another week. You've been handed portions of Chapter 3 of a report carrying a bizarrely optimistic title. The folder holds some pages of manuscript with handwritten additions and what is apparently a finished version of those pages. The finished pages have been reproduced in some fashion that is unfamiliar to you. You are to proofread the finished pages against the manuscript.

Everything old was once new. When we composed this exercise, we hoped that, without being told what to look for, you would identify the kinds of errors typical of scanning technology. Thus we went out of our way to invent an editor who had never heard of this process. Who hadn't seen a scanned document by the mid-1990s? To answer this question and have some fun, we postulated a harried editor in the last days of the Soviet Union.

Note: The page proofs for your use appear on pages 188–191 and the manuscript on pages 192–196.

EX TENEBRIS LOX; THE BRIGHT FUTURE AHEAD. A Report Delivered to Mikhail Sergeievich Gorbachev, President of the USSR, August 4, 1991

Mikhail Sergeievich1
We have accelerated the production of this report in order to have it ready for you to take to your dacha. We are proud to be making use for the first time of the new "scanning" technology that we have imported from Hungary. It has enabled the Committee to copy onto disk the typewritten manuscript and print its entire text with outstanding accuracy and speed — a fonn of "top-desk publishing", one might say.
Wishing you and your family a restful and productive vac@tion,

The Committee of Economic Advisers

....

Chapter 3: An Overview of RLH-Sector Balance Sheets

The Union government's debt may get most of the attention, but it is the RLH sector -- the republican,   local and hospital sector — that is responsible for about a quarter of the net debt, which amounted to more than 7O percent of GDP in 1989. This, we should note, came at the end of a time of eoonomic expansion. The deterioration in the RLH sector's debt position since the 1976s has been nearly as severe as that of the Union government itse1f.
RLH-sector balance sheets showed more "red ink" (as they say(in all regions over the past decade and a half as the fiscal policies of all republics became less prudent. The "have-not" republics may have had the worst net-debt-to-GDP ratios, but there was still considerable variation in pertonnance. As a matter   of fact, Byelorussia, the Ukraine and Kazabrlah23swan!amassive jump in their ratios, while the less-advantaged Central Asian republlcs changed very little. (See Table 3.1 for the example of Uzbekistsn, which remained in surplus for several consecutive years.) Lithuania, despite its
superior economic strength and its outstanding growth perfonnance in the 1980s, underachieved badly in reducing the pressure on domestic saving and supporting national anti-infiation policies. (The Oommittee has decided, after long deliberations, on the usefulness of the economic ooncept "infiation" in a restricted sense for describing certain tendencies present in the Union   economy. See Appendix A.) Relatively prosperous

Estonia and Latvia contributed surprisingly to the a88regate decline in the financial health of the RLH sector at various times over the past 15 years. This is in contrast to the situation from 1972 to 1977, when the PLH sectors of the three Baltic republics had healthy surpluses. with Estonia's averaging well over 6 percent of republican GOP. Strange to say = in the context of a command economy — even Byelorussia, though somewhat disadvantaged as compared to the latter three republics, could have done more to restrain its expenditure growth and the concurrent debt escalation this entalled (see Figure 1.1).

The failure to achieve a more decisive reduction in republican debt levels during the 1980s has left the less- advantaged republics with a painful choice: taking politically difficult action to restrain the cgclical deficit rise caused by the recession-like circumstances (among ourselves , we may speak frankly of these matters), or allowing their debt ratios to move upwards, and so incurring lowered credit ratings. These two options are what we shall explone in this chapter.

* * * *

Most economists are how aware of the Union government's continuing deficits and enonnous debt. "The public debt must go down!" is a cry that we have begun to hear. "The public dobt must be made public!" is another. (It must be remembered that the gold reserves that have supported the value of the ruble have been seriously depleted of late.> Political leaders have had to take [unpopular measures and engage in propaganda offensives, while academics turn out numerous studies on the results, circumstances and possible solutions.

Often overlooked in the context of the debt is the fact that "public" is not synonymous with "central government". We enjoy three levels of government — federal, republlcan and local — as well as a huge quast-public sector in which schools and hospitals fonnn by far the largest part. Even though the federal government net debt constitutes the largest potion of the public debt, developments in ether layers of the public sector - republican and local governments and hospitals — have been a key element in the picture. They continue to be so. Failure to foous on this element leads many observers to miss   the *federal nature of the public debt and as a oonsequence encourages the republics to evade responsibility in finding a solution.*

This report hopes to remedy that oversighc by examining the financial situation of the PLH sector in the context of the Onion as federation. The final portion of the chapter comprises a brief background review plus an introduction to some of the analytical problems involved.

Accounting and Accountability

A few words on the handling of data are in order before entering upon the detailed analysts found in this and subsequent chapters. We need to decide what data are to be recorded in which categories. We need to know now to distinguish between capital and current costs (for example, should museums be counted as investment in   fixed capital? What about investment in human resources   — in education, training, health care?). We must decide too how to handle inflation in the public sector (what statistics are hest presented in current rubles? in constant rubles?). We need to decide what is an asset and what is a liabillty. Finally. we need to determine what is the purpose of public accounting. If it is true that its purpose is to tell the people, as well as telling their representatives, how their money is raised and spent, and not to obfuscate, then some fundamental refonns are clearly in   order.

The rest of this chapter deals with the first point.   Few of the problems in analyzing the RLH sector arise from a paucity of data. Indeed, the data we typically assemble presents an *embarras de richesses,* raising the questions of what do do with all the information and how to ensure that it is all comparable.

The government assembles both Series A data and Series B data. These series are distinguished primarily by orientatione Series A analysis sees the government primarily as a provider of services, while Series B analysis defines government as an actor in the economy. Series A data are in current rubles only: some Series Я data are available in conatant rubles as well. Series A data are divided by functional category: education, health care, policing, etc. They do not distinguish between current and capital transactions. The categories for Series 8 data are economic: expenditure, consumption spending, capital fonnation, transfers and interoat on the public debt.

Thus, details on expenditure are available only in current rubles, and their analysis tends to overstate the ratio of total govermnent expenditure to GOP in contrast with a comparable analysis done in constant rubles. The implication is, of course, that inflation in the govermnent sector has exceeded overall infiation — a point to be discussed later on in this study.

Table 3.1: RLH-Sector Revenue and Expenditure, 1986-1989: Uzbekistan

	1988	1987	1988	1989
	(milllons of rubles)			
Revenue				
Direct taxes on persons	9,599	1L336	13,378	14,186
Direct taxes on gov't enterprises	Q284	2,526	2,B14	2,718
Indirect taxes	17,A72	19,AST	21,539	24,150
Other transfers from persons	2,174	2,271	Q386	2,562
Investment income	3,278	3,399	3,561	3,8OS
Transfers from federal gov't	4,816	5,188	5,486	5,657
Current revenue	*39,603*	*44,177*	*49,124*	*53,061*
Capital consumptton allowance		1,942	2,022	2,148 2,287
Total revenue	*41,5A5*	*46,199*	*51,272*	*55,348*
Expenditure				
Current goods and services	26,TIS	28,931	3L674	34,637
Transfers to persons	S,798	6,558	7,269	7,977
Other transfers	S96	1,097	L154	1,245
Interest on public debt	4,872	5,096	5,369	5,619
Current expenditure	*88,281*	*A1,682*	*45,466*	*49,478*
Capital formation	2,839	3,478	3,957	4,103
Total expenditure	*Al,l20*	*45,160*	*49,423*	*53,581*
Surplus (deflcit)	425	L039	3,848	1,767

EX TENEBRIS LUX: THE BRIGHT FUTURE AHEAD. A Report
Delivered to Mikhail Sergeievich Gorbachev, President
of the USSR, August 4, 1991

Mikhail Sergeievich!
     We have accelerated the production of this report
in order to have it ready for you to take to your
dacha. We are proud to be making use for the first time
of the new "scanning" technology that we have imported
from Hungary. It has enabled the Committee to copy onto
disk the typewritten manuscript and print its entire
text with outstanding accuracy and speed -- a form of
"top-desk publishing", one might say.
     Wishing you and your family a restful and
productive vacation,

                    The Committee of Economic Advisers
          . . . .

Chapter 3: An Overview of RLH-Sector Balance Sheets

The Union government's debt may get most of the
attention, but it is the RLH sector -- the republican,
local and hospital sector -- that is responsible for
about a quarter of the net debt, which amounted to more
than 70 percent of GDP in 1989. This, we should note,
came at the end of a time of economic expansion. The
deterioration in the RLH sector's debt position since
the 1970s has been nearly as severe as that of the
Union government itself.
     RLH-sector balance sheets showed more "red ink"
(as they say) in all regions over the past decade and a
half as the fiscal policies of all republics became
less prudent. The "have-not" republics may have had the
worst net-debt-to-GDP ratios, but there was still
considerable variation in performance. As a matter of
fact, Byelorussia, [confirm] the Ukraine and Kazakhstan
underwent a massive jump in their ratios, while the
less-advantaged Central Asian republics changed very
little. (See Table 3.1 for the example of Uzbekistan,
which remained in surplus for several consecutive
years.) Lithuania, despite its superior economic
strength and its outstanding growth performance in the
1980s, underachieved badly in reducing the pressure on
domestic saving and supporting national anti-inflation
policies. (The Committee has decided, after long
deliberations, on the usefulness of the economic

concept "inflation" in a restricted sense for
describing certain tendencies present in the Union
economy. See Appendix A.) Relatively prosperous Estonia
and Latvia contributed surprisingly to the aggregate
decline in the financial health of the RLH sector at
various times over the past 15 years. This is in
contrast to the situation from 1972 to 1977, when the
RLH sectors of the three Baltic republics had healthy
surpluses, with Estonia's averaging well over 6 percent
of republican GDP. Strange to say -- in the context of
a command economy -- even Byelorussia, though somewhat
disadvantaged as compared to the latter three
republics, could have done more to restrain its
expenditure growth and the concurrent debt escalation
this entailed (see Figure 1.1).

The failure to achieve a more decisive reduction
in republican debt levels during the 1980s has left the
less-advantaged republics with a painful choice: taking
politically difficult action to restrain the cyclical
deficit rise caused by the recession-like circumstances
(among ourselves, we may speak frankly of these
matters), or allowing their debt ratios to move
upwards, and so incurring lowered credit ratings. These
two options are what we shall explore in this chapter.

* * * *

Most economists are now aware of the Union government's
continuing deficits and enormous debt. "The public debt
must go down!" is a cry that we have begun to hear.
"The public debt must be made public!" is another. (It
must be remembered that the gold reserves that have
supported the value of the ruble have been seriously
depleted of late.) Political leaders have had to take
[confirm??] unpopular measures and engage in
propaganda offensives, while academics turn out
numerous studies on the results, circumstances and
possible solutions.

Often overlooked in the context of the debt is the
fact that "public" is not synonymous with "central
government". We enjoy three levels of government --
federal, republican and local -- as well as a huge
quasi-public sector in which schools and hospitals form
by far the largest part. Even though the federal
government net debt constitutes the largest potion of
the public debt, developments in other layers of the
public sector -- republican and local governments and
hospitals -- have been a key element in the picture.

90 They continue to be so. Failure to focus on this
element leads many observers to miss the *federal*
nature of the public debt and as a consequence
encourages the republics to evade responsibility in
finding a solution.
95 This report hopes to remedy that oversight by
examining the financial situation of the PLH sector in
the context of the Union as federation. The final
portion of the chapter comprises a brief background
review plus an introduction to some of the analytical
100 problems involved.

Accounting and Accountability

A few words on the handling of data are in order before
entering upon the detailed analysis found in this and
subsequent chapters. We need to decide what data are to
105 be recorded in which categories. We need to know now to
distinguish between capital and current costs (for
example, should museums be counted as investment in
fixed capital? What about investment in human resources
-- in education, training, health care?). We must
110 decide too how to handle inflation in the public sector
(what statistics are best presented in current rubles?
in constant rubles?). We need to decide what is an
asset and what is a liability. Finally, we need to
determine what is the purpose of public accounting. If
115 it is true that its purpose is to tell the people, as
well as telling their representatives, how their money
is raised and spent, and not to obfuscate, then some
fundamental reforms are clearly in order.
The rest of this chapter deals with the first
120 point.
Few of the problems in analyzing the RLH sector
arise from a paucity of data. Indeed, the data we
typically assemble presents an *embarras de richesses*,
raising the questions of what do do with all the
125 information and how to ensure that it is all
comparable.
The government assembles both Series A data and
Series B data. These series are distinguished primarily
by orientation: Series A analysis sees the government
130 primarily as a provider of services, while Series B
analysis defines government as an actor in the economy.
Series A data are in current rubles only; some Series B
data are available in constant rubles as well. Series A
data are divided by functional category: education,
135 health care, policing, etc. They do not distinguish

between current and capital transactions. The
categories for Series B data are economic: expenditure,
consumption spending, capital formation, transfers and
interest on the public debt.

140   Thus, details on expenditure are available only in
current rubles, and their analysis tends to overstate
the ratio of total govermnent expenditure to GDP in
contrast with a comparable analysis done in constant
rubles. The implication is, of course, that inflation
145 in the government sector has exceeded overall inflation
-- a point to be discussed later on in this study.

```
-------------------------------------------------------------------

Table 3.1:    RLH-Sector Revenue and Expenditure,
              1986-1989: Uzbekistan

                                  1986     1987     1988     1989
                                        (millions of rubles)

Revenue
Direct taxes on persons          9,599   11,336   13,378   14,166
Direct taxes on gov't
     enterprises                 2,264    2,526    2,814    2,718
Indirect taxes                  17,472   19,457   21,539   24,150
Other transfers from persons     2,174    2,271    2,366    2,562
Investment income                3,278    3,399    3,561    3,808
Transfers from federal gov't     4,816    5,188    5,466    5,657
Current revenue                 39,603   44,177   49,124   53,061
Capital consumption allowance    1,942    2,022    2,148    2,287

Total revenue                   41,545   46,199   51,272   55,348


Expenditure
Current goods and services      26,715   28,931   31,674   34,637
Transfers to persons             5,798    6,558    7,269    7,977
Other transfers                    896    1,097    1,154    1,245
Interest on public debt          4,872    5,096    5,369    5,619
Current expenditure             38,281   41,682   45,466   49,478
Capital formation                2,839    3,478    3,957    4,103

Total expenditure               41,120   45,160   49,423   53,581


Surplus (deficit)                  425    1,039    3,848    1,767


-------------------------------------------------------------------
```

The Bosun's Chair

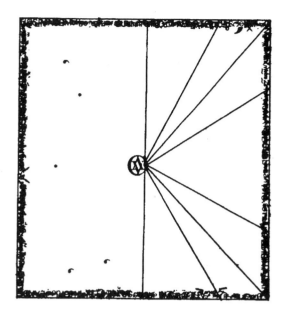

Your firm produces print materials for a variety of trade associations. Each client is responsible for editing—including copy editing—its own publications. Your company's policy is that only minimal changes should be made without consulting the appropriate managing editor.

Copy has already been edited when your firm receives an article. Bert, the desktop operator, does any necessary input and then sets the material up in pages according to the specs for that publication. He makes no initial attempt at making the copy fit—that's your job.

Today Bert gives you the following spread as the first proof of an article for a monthly that's running a little late. Its editor is not available, so you need to solve the obvious copyfitting problems without help. The client has instructed you never to change the size of advertisements and photos or the positions of sidebars and pull quotes.

THE ▪ COMMON ▪ ELEMENTS

By Brian Buchanan, P.Eng., and Robert Cardarelli, P.Eng.

Bosun's Chair Used for Surface Review of Walls

DO YOU FEEL CONFIDENT about the information you have on the current state of your condominium building's exterior walls? Do you understand the life-cycle costing and budgeting required for exterior condominium building maintenance? Do you have a strategy for both the short-term and long-term maintenance of your building walls? Are you experiencing problems with your condominium building's exterior but don't know the source, the cause or the extent of the problem, not to mention the potential remedies and costs to correct the problem?

If you need the answer to any of these questions, consider the use of a bosun's chair, commonly used by window cleaners, to provide you with the required answers in a timely and cost-effective manner.

The building science professional who is called upon to investigate reported problems with the exterior walls of a highrise condominium building is a professional who will investigate by addressing the functional unity of the condominium building's exterior wall assembly and its individual components. This can include the cladding material (e.g., bricks, metal panels, stucco, stone, precast or cast-in-place concrete, etc.), glazing or curtain wall systems, joint sealants, the air/vapour barrier details, and thermal insulation details of the wall system. Along with a review of design/construction documents, the condominium building's wall must be examined on the surface and, where required, in detail through test openings.

Sampling Wall Strips

Traditionally, the building science professional would access highrise condominium building walls by sampling one or two vertical wall strips or "drops" via a swingstage. The reason for this limited type of sampling is primarily due to the charges for swingstage setup/dismantling and hourly rental charges. Another disadvantage of this type of review procedure is that it is limited to the wall area where the swingstage is set up. Review of other wall areas with the same swingstage will require additional setup charges and charges for the swingstage rental for each drop location. Normally, it is not possible to conduct more than two or three swingstage drops in a day, but this depends upon the height of the condominium building, the complexity of setup and the level of detail required of the survey. An alternative, cost-saving procedure for the surface review of exterior walls of highrise condominium buildings is through the use of the bosun's chair, used for window-washing activities, that originated on ships for rigging ropes and sails. This method not only allows a single investigator to review the wall surface quickly and cost-effectively, but allows for a larger sampling of the wall surface area in the same time it would take for one swingstage drop.

Swingstage Cost: $2,000

For example, a review of the exterior walls of a 20-storey condominium building by swingstage procedure would cost in the order of $2,000 for two swingstage drops done during one to two days, without test openings in the exterior wall. This would, however, only cover the review of approximately 10–15% of the condominium building's total surface wall area (depending on stage width). By using the bosun's chair, the same $2,000 cost would allow for a review of 80–100% of the condominium building's wall surface area, with no requirement for swingstage. By comparison, an owner would require an expenditure of $12,000 to $20,000 for an 80–100% review of the condominium building's wall surface area by swingstage.

Additional advantages in favour of the bosun's chair procedure are that it would allow the investigator to assess the extent of surface problems more accurately, especially where quantities are needed for future unit price repairs. Outside contractors are also not required, which can eliminate some of the time delays and confusion which occasionally influence projects such as these.

There are, however, some limitations to the utility of a bosun's chair. The primary disadvantage is that it is unsafe to attempt to make all but the most minor of test openings in the wall cladding because the suspension and life-line ropes are too easily damaged. The bosun's chair is also not recommended for investigative use where the descent exceeds 90 m or 300 ft. (win-

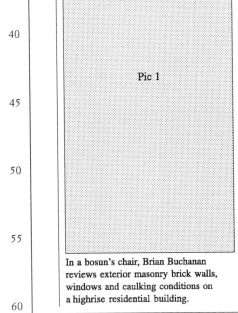

In a bosun's chair, Brian Buchanan reviews exterior masonry brick walls, windows and caulking conditions on a highrise residential building.

dow cleaners are not permitted to exceed this limit).

The use of a bosun's chair will not eliminate the need to use a swingstage or scaffolding to conduct test openings from the exterior into the wall system, where required. However, the charges for the swingstage-test openings requirement would be the same additional charge whether the bosun's chair or the swingstage is used for the surface review of exterior walls.

Safety Anchors

While condition surveys and cladding investigations done by suspended equipment may not be required to conform to the same regulation which governs window cleaning, the roof must be equipped with window-cleaning safety anchors. These anchors must meet the Ministry of Labour (MOL) guidelines and regulations, specifically Ontario Regulation 527/88, which came into effect on August 18, 1988. Sections 39 through 41 of this regulation detail the legislated duties

Pic 2

The importance of properly installed and inspected safety anchors for both primary support and fall-arrest systems cannot be overemphasized when using the bosun's chair.

of the building owner, in this case the condominium corporation. These duties (relating to window cleaning by suspended equipment) may be briefly summarized as follows:

• The building owner shall prepare a sketch showing all anchor points on the building suitable and adequate for the attachment of suspended equipment (support line) and independent safety life line, and post this sketch at the roof entrance. It is recommended that the sketch be reviewed by an engineer.

• A copy of the sketch is to be provided to the window-washing contractor and a copy is to be posted on the building near the entrance to the roof.

• The building owner shall cause all anchor points to be inspected by a competent person prior to their initial use and at least once a year in accordance with section 41 of the regulation and ensure that faulty anchors/situations are repaired. Inspections must be recorded in a logbook.

• The building owner shall ensure that faulty anchors are repaired. Repairs should be recorded in the inspection logbook and noted on the roof sketch.

Despite the use of two primary suspension lines and an independent safety life line, the importance of safety anchors to provide a basis for both a primary support and a fall-arrest system cannot be overemphasized. Even today, we continually find anchors which are woefully inadequate to meet the intent of the MOL and CSA Standard CAN/CSA-Z91-M90 (for newer buildings).

Whether you require an investiga-

tion of existing problems with the exterior walls of your highrise condominium building, or need an inspection for establishing a preventive maintenance plan and/or reserve fund plan, the bosun's chair roped-access survey method can provide competent and certified building science professionals with a procedure that may save you initial investigation costs and could save significant future restorative costs.

Brian Buchanan and Robert Cardarelli are engineers with the Trow Consulting Engineers Ltd., Toronto office.

Editor: Article, byline, and sidebar spill over 9 lines. Caption for Pic 2 is also too long. – Bert

Ad 1

A Teacher's Manual

Your new employer, a large publisher of textbooks, is preparing a teacher's manual to accompany a language arts series for elementary schools. The production editor is incommunicado in hospital; the doctor mutters something unintelligible about sensory overload. You have been asked to check these pages. The text was prepared on disk, and you have been told that before it went to the in-house desk-topper, it was carefully edited and proofed (a statement you take with a grain of salt). Your job is primarily to check format. When you ask the desktopper for the marked-up hard copy that she worked from, she reports that after the first 30 pages the only instructions she needed were to "follow style". A search through the editor's desk has revealed no style sheet and no design specifications.

You also ask for copies of the student material referred to in these pages, but you receive the answer you half expect: the book is in production and won't be available for another three weeks at least. The managing editor suggests that you address all queries to the project's content editor, who has worked closely with the production and design departments. He will be checking the pages after you have been through them and can convey to the appropriate person any queries he can't answer himself.

1 *I ntroducing* THE GOLDEN WOODS

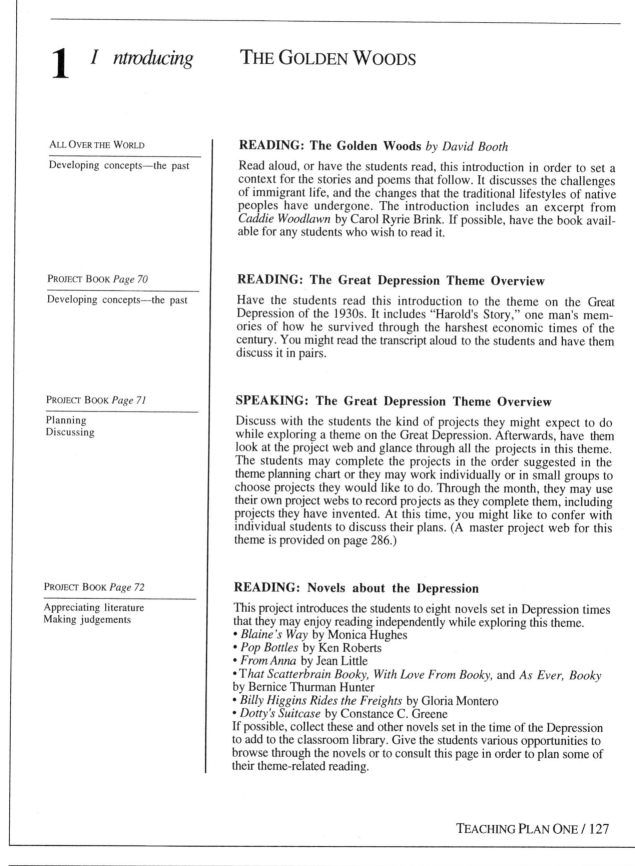

ALL OVER THE WORLD

Developing concepts—the past

READING: The Golden Woods *by David Booth*

Read aloud, or have the students read, this introduction in order to set a context for the stories and poems that follow. It discusses the challenges of immigrant life, and the changes that the traditional lifestyles of native peoples have undergone. The introduction includes an excerpt from *Caddie Woodlawn* by Carol Ryrie Brink. If possible, have the book available for any students who wish to read it.

PROJECT BOOK *Page 70*

Developing concepts—the past

READING: The Great Depression Theme Overview

Have the students read this introduction to the theme on the Great Depression of the 1930s. It includes "Harold's Story," one man's memories of how he survived through the harshest economic times of the century. You might read the transcript aloud to the students and have them discuss it in pairs.

PROJECT BOOK *Page 71*

Planning
Discussing

SPEAKING: The Great Depression Theme Overview

Discuss with the students the kind of projects they might expect to do while exploring a theme on the Great Depression. Afterwards, have them look at the project web and glance through all the projects in this theme. The students may complete the projects in the order suggested in the theme planning chart or they may work individually or in small groups to choose projects they would like to do. Through the month, they may use their own project webs to record projects as they complete them, including projects they have invented. At this time, you might like to confer with individual students to discuss their plans. (A master project web for this theme is provided on page 286.)

PROJECT BOOK *Page 72*

Appreciating literature
Making judgements

READING: Novels about the Depression

This project introduces the students to eight novels set in Depression times that they may enjoy reading independently while exploring this theme.
• *Blaine's Way* by Monica Hughes
• *Pop Bottles* by Ken Roberts
• *From Anna* by Jean Little
• *That Scatterbrain Booky, With Love From Booky,* and *As Ever, Booky* by Bernice Thurman Hunter
• *Billy Higgins Rides the Freights* by Gloria Montero
• *Dotty's Suitcase* by Constance C. Greene
If possible, collect these and other novels set in the time of the Depression to add to the classroom library. Give the students various opportunities to browse through the novels or to consult this page in order to plan some of their theme-related reading.

TEACHING PLAN ONE / 127

TEACHER ANTHOLOGY
Pages 77–81

Appreciating literature

LISTENING: The Root Cellar *by Janet Lunn*

Read aloud this novel excerpt in which Rose, an orphan sent to live with relatives she does not know, meets a woman who "shifts" from the past. Rose herself then "shifts" herself into the past. Accompanying discussion and storytelling activities are suggested. This selection serves as an interesting introduction to the excerpt from *Shadow in Hawthorn Bay,* also by Janet Lunn, in which the heroine, Mary, has an unusual power—the ability to see into the past, the future, and to places far away.

2 *Exploring* THE GOLDEN WOODS

ALL OVER THE WORLD
Pages 122–135

READING: Shadow in Hawthorn Bay *by Janet Lunn*

About the Author
Janet Lunn is originally from Dallas, Texas, but now lives in Hillier, Ontario. She studied at Queen's University in Kingston, Ontario, has worked as an editor of children's literature in Toronto and served as the writer-in-residence at the Regina Public Library. In addition to her novels for children, she writes scripts for the Canadian Broadcasting Corporation and short stories for periodicals. Her books include *The Twelve Dancing Princesses*, *The Root Cellar*, and *Shadow in Hawthorn Bay*.

Writing for children gives her a chance "to get to the roots of an idea. As well," she admits," under my middle-aged skin, I am really ten years old."

Reporting on past or present experiences

Before the Selection
1. Students who have moved with their families to places far from friends and other relatives might share their experiences with the rest of the group.

Locating information
Recalling and sharing information

2. Explain to the students that southern and central Ontario were known in he early 1800s as Upper Canada. The students might look at a map of the world to see where Scotland is in relation to Upper Canada. The students might also share anything they know about either place in 1812.

128 / TEACHING PLANS ONE AND TWO

ALL OVER THE WORLD
Pages 122–135

TAPE 5 *Side A*

Making inferences
Understanding character

Locating information
Making comparisons

Noting illustrator's style

Using context clues
Developing vocabulary

Appreciating literature

STUDENT BOOK *Page 41*

Making comparisons
Organizing information

Experiencing the Selection

1. For some students, read aloud the first four paragraphs (to "And barely a word since.") and discuss the following briefly:.
   —Do you think Mary really heard Duncan's voice?
   —Why might Duncan be calling?
   —Why do you think Mary is not surprised to hear his voice?
   —Is it possible to hear someone calling from "three thousand miles away"?
   You might then read aloud the rest of the story.

2. Some students might listen to the story on the tape .

3. Some students might read the story in pairs, reading alternate paragraphs. (One person should read the entire letter from Duncan.)

4. Some students might read the story independently.

> *1, 2,* and *3* are suitable for developing readers.
> *3* and *4* are suitable for independent readers.
> Most developing readers will be able to read the selection independently after experiencing the other methods.

Responding to the Selection

1. Mary thought constantly about Duncan, but he only wrote one brief letter to her. Have the students discuss the following in small groups or as one large group:
   —Why might Duncan not have written more often?
   —Why do you think Mary hated the letter so?
   —Why do you think Mary still missed Duncan so much?
   The students might ask themselves again the questions from Experiencing the Selection 1 about Duncan calling Mary and her lack of surprise at this.

2. Have the students list the information in the story about life and traditions in Scotland in the 1800s and give comparable information about Canada at that time. They might then discuss and write about the adjustments Duncan would have had to make in Upper Canada in 1812.

3. Have the students examine the illustrations accompanying the story.
   —How might you describe Brian McPhee's style?
   —How is this style suitable for the story's setting?

5. If possible, have the novel *Shadow in Hawthorn Bay* available for those who would like to read further.

6. **Reflections of One Another**
   The students list similarities and differences between Duncan and Mary. On completion, they might share their responses with a partner.

7. **The An Dà Shellad**
   The students use information from the story and their own ideas to explain how Mary's apparent "gift" of the two sights might be both a gift and a misfortune. They then debate the two views with a partner, switching sides.

TEACHING PLAN TWO / 129

3 *Exploring* THE GOLDEN WOODS

Classifying
Expanding on the text

TAPE 5 *Side A*

Appreciating literature

SHARED READING
Transparency Six–29
Manual Page 24

Choral reading
Using literary patterns

8. **The Old Ones**

Mary's environment is one rich with stories and folklore. The students list beliefs held by some people in the story that they would classify as superstitions, and then list other superstitions they know. They share their lists with a partner, and are invited to do further research into the origins of superstitions. (The students may note that Mary lives near Loch Ness and mention the monster reputed to live there.)

LISTENING: Shadow in Hawthorn Bay *by Janet Lunn*

Those students who have not already done so may enjoy listening to the story on tape.

CHORAL DRAMATIZATION: A Chorale of Cherokee Night Music as Heard through an Open Window in Summer Long Ago *by Jonathan Williams*

This poem reproduces the sounds of animals that may be heard on a summer night. (The animals are identified in the manual.) Accompanying activities involve the students in silent reading, choral reading, movement, and creating sound collages. (If possible, provide several tape recorders, so that small groups of students may to record their sound collages.) This poem can be used to emphasize the strangeness and the mystery of "the land dark with forest," so different from the Scottish highlands portrayed in "Shadow in Hawthorn Bay."

4 *Exploring* THE GOLDEN WOODS

PROJECT BOOK *Pages 92—96*

EXTENDING: More and More Projects

Have the students browse through this section and choose one of these five projects to do. For some of them, they may need to work in pairs or small groups.

130 / TEACHING PLAN THREE AND FOUR

Collaborating
Asking questions

Speaking: Jeopardy

The students work in groups of six to design a Jeopardy-style game in which contestants must formulate questions for given answers. The Project Book game focuses on periods in history, including the Depression. When the groups have designed their games they might try them out with other groups. (Students will need index cards for this project.)

PROJECT BOOK *Page 93*

Collaborating

Speaking: Monopoly

The students learn how the game Monopoly became the rage during the Depression and play the game *or* create versions of the game based on landmarks in their own community. They might play these new games and then revise their games according to the players' responses.

PROJECT BOOK *Page 94*

Projecting into the experiences of others

Research: Depression Fare

The students list ingredients used to prepare meals and eliminate from their lists those unavailable in most Depression era homes. Then they plan and prepare meals for a family during the Depression, perhaps to. share on a "Depression Fare" day.

PROJECT BOOK *Page 95*

Making comparisons
Organizing information

Research: The Weekly Food Bill

The students examine a Depression era food bill and find the current cost of the listed items *or* use grocery flyers to prepare a weekly shopping list for a family today, keeping the total cost under $50.

PROJECT BOOK *Page 96*

Researching
Writing in various modes—stories, scripts

Writing: Favourite Decade

Groups of students each choose a decade in the twentieth century that they would like to travel back to. They gather information from books and interviews, write stories, and plan short plays based on their stories. Groups might combine the plays into a twentieth-century pageant.

PROJECT BOOK *Page 85–86*

Projecting into the experiences of others
Writing in various modes—letters

WRITING: Letters to R. B. Bennett
The students first read two letters written to the Prime Minister Bennett during the 1930s. They then choose from the following activities:
• as Prime Minister Bennett, write a reply to one of the letters and compare the advice given with that given by classmates;
• plan and write letters expressing personal concerns to politicians and mail the final copies. (The students are reminded to check that they're writing to the appropriate persons.)

TEACHING PLAN FOUR / 131

5 *Exploring* THE GOLDEN WOODS

All Over the World
Pages 136–145

READING: Death over Montreal *by Geoffrey Bilson*

About the Author

When Geoffrey Bilson was a child growing up in Cardiff, Wales, he and his brother produced a family magazine, his first publishing venture. After settling in Canada, he wrote Goodbye Sarah for his daughter Kate. This was his first widely published novel and was eventually translated into French. As his ambitions proved to be for a larger audience, he went on to write Death over Montreal and Hockeybat Harris. At the time of his death in 1987, he was teaching history at the University of Saskatchewan.

Hypothesizing
Recalling and sharing information

Before the Selection
1. Have the students, in groups, list and discuss problems that immigrants to Canada in the early 1800s might have had.
   —What might these immigrants have experienced.
   —How might things be different for immigrants today?
   Students who have recently immigrated or who know recent immigrants might discuss these experiences with the others.

Developing concepts

2. If possible, show the film *Megan Carey* to the students. (See Resource List, page 000.) This film features Megan, who comes to Canada during the potato famine of the 1840s and will set a context for Mrs. Douglas and Jamie's experiences of about the same time.

ALL OVER THE WORLD
Pages 136–145

Experiencing the Selection
1. Groups of students might read the story in role as narrator, Mrs. Douglas, Jamie, carter, priest, cathedral woman, three society women, landlady, and Mr. Johnson. (Students might read more than one role.)

2. Some students might read the story in pairs, one reading narration, the other dialogue. For a second reading, they might switch parts.

3. Some students might read the story independently.

> 1 and 2 are suitable for developing readers.
> 2 and 3 are suitable for independent readers.
> Most developing readers will be able to read the selection independently after experiencing the other methods.

Recognizing problems and their solutions
Hypothesizing

Responding to the Selection
1. The story tells of a series of disasters that befall one family among many new to Montreal in the 1830s. Have the students look back through the story and list the major events. Then ask: "How do Mrs. Douglas and Jamie cope with each disaster?" They might consider what might happen in each case if the story were taking place today.

132 / TEACHING PLAN FIVE

Making inferences
Making judgements
Role-playing

2. Discuss with the students the scene with the committee of the Ladies Beneficient Society.
 —What kinds of questions are the women asking?
 —What are their reasons for asking these kinds of questions?
 —Do you think Mrs. Douglas is right to send the women away?
 —If you give money to help people, do you think you have a right to question them about their lives? Why or why not?
 The students might work in groups to decide how they, as members of a charitable committee, should dispense money to needy people offered by a benevolent donor. They might draw up guidelines for their committee and share them with other groups.

Expanding on the text

3. At the end of the story, Mrs. Douglas has an idea that might help them. Have the students work in small groups to plan and write a next chapter for the story.

Discussing
Researching

4. The students might discuss in groups, or as a class, what they have learned about life in Canada in the early 1800s from this story. Some of the students might be interested in finding more information about this period, and making a display or giving a presentation to the class.

Appreciating literature

5. If possible, have the novel *Death over Montreal* available for those who would like to read further.

STUDENT BOOK
Page 44
Recognizing emotion
Explaining

6. **On Their Own**
 The students list examples of emotions displayed by Mrs. Douglas and Jamie, and explain when and why they felt them. They compare notes with a classmate.

STUDENT BOOK
Page 45
Recognizing cause-and-effect relationships
Explaining

7. **Reasons**
 The students find evidence in the story and their own ideas to give reasons for some of the actions and events.

6 *Exploring* THE GOLDEN WOODS

STUDENT BOOK *Page 46*
Solving problems
Expressing personal opinions

8. **"A Liar and a Cheat"**
 The students suggest ways Jamie might try to get the money back from Mr. Johnson. They then conduct a survey to discover the class's feelings about Mr. Johnson, and what their ideas are about recovering the money.

TEACHING PLAN FIVE AND SIX / 133

PROJECT BOOK *Pages 81–82*

Choral reading
Discussing
Using literary patterns

SPEAKING: The Wind Our Enemy *by Anne Marriott*

The students read a poem about some prairie-dwellers' efforts to forget their hardships during the Depression. They then work in groups of four or five to:
• read the poem chorally;
• discuss what the poem tells about life in the Depression;
• write poems to be read fifty years from now about their childhood life; present group readings or display the poems.

PROJECT BOOK *Page 71*

Planning
Discussing

SPEAKING: The Great Depression Theme Overview

Have the students review the project web and browse through the projects in this theme. Ask them to record on their own project webs the projects they have already completed. Remind them to include ones they have invented for themselves. They might choose other projects they would like to do, and at this time, you might wish to confer with individual students to discuss their plans. (A master project web for this theme is provided on page 000)

7 *Exploring*   THE GOLDEN WOODS

PROJECT BOOK *Pages 88–89*

Analyzing picture information

VIEWING: Where's Waldo?

The students analyze an action-filled illustration of a museum that in cludes Waldo, a travelling student. The students then choose from the two follow-up activities.
• find Waldo, and list interesting things Waldo might have seen in the museum and compare lists in pairs,
• examine the illustration for articles of the twentieth century.

PROJECT BOOK
Page 91

Noting parts of speech

LANGUAGE STUDY: In the Past

The students rewrite twenty-six verbs in the past tense.

134 / TEACHING PLANS SIX AND SEVEN

TAPE 5 *Side B*

Appreciating music

LISTENING: Songs of Yesteryear

Students listen to a medley of tunes of songs from the past and are invited to identify them.

Answers
"The Bells Are Ringing for Me and My Girl"
"Cruising Down the River"
"Ja Da, Ja Da"
"Hello My Baby"
"In the Good Old Summer Time"
"Take Me out to the Ball Game"
"Daisy, Daisy"
"Roll out the Barrel"

Organizing information

The students might plan and record a collection of present-day tunes as a "Songs of Today" tape. They might play the compilation for other students to identify. Alternatively, each student in turn might hum a few bars of a tune while the others try to identify it.

SHARED READING
Transparency Six–31
Manual Page 25

Choral reading
Using literary formats

CHORAL DRAMATIZATION: An Indian Summer Day on the Prairie
by Vachel Lindsay

This selection describes the sun's progress through the eyes of the people of the Great Plains. Accompanying activities involve the students in choral reading, brainstorming, and patterning. The poem shows a contrasting relationship with the sun to that of the upcoming Inuit selections in this theme.

8 *Exploring* THE GOLDEN WOODS

ALL OVER THE WORLD
Pages 146 –147

READING: Magic Words to Bring Luck When Hunting Caribou *from the Netsilik Inuit* and **Sadness** *from the Ammassalik Inuit*

Magic Words to Bring Luck When Hunting Caribou

TEACHING PLAN ONE / 135

Before the Selection

Appreciating literature
Making associations

1. Read to the students or recall for them the following Inuit selections from *Over the Mountain*:
   —"Magic Words to Feel Better" (page 223)
   —"Pitseolak: Pictures Out of My Life" (page 232)
   The students might also reread these poems from another hunting culture in *All Over the World* and recall their discussions:
   —"Black-Tailed Deer Song" (page 22)
   —"Song of the Hunter" (page 23)

Recalling and sharing
information

2. Have the students share their knowledge of the Inuit, their way of life, and in particular their hunting as a source of the materials for food, tools, and shelter. They might consider how traditional lifestyles have survived or been adapted to the "modern" world.

Developing vocabulary

3. Discuss the difference between the following languages: "the people" or "the real people";
   —"Eskimo," meaning in the language of the Algonquins "eaters of raw meat" and seen by the Inuit as derogatory;
   The students might consider the power of names (as in name-calling, and one's attachment to one's own name) and the importance of respecting others' preferred forms of their names.

Experiencing the Selection

ALL OVER THE WORLD
Page 146

1. Read aloud the poem, having first assigned duplicate phrases (great swan, great caribou bull, come here) to be read aloud by pairs or groups of students joining in with the reading.

2. The students might read the poem chorally:
   —in unison;
   —with lines assigned to groups and individuals.

3. The students might work in small groups to plan and present oral readings of the poem.

4. The students might read the poem independently.

> All the students should experience the poem using various methods.

Responding to the Selection

Recognizing central meaning

Discuss with the students what this poem suggests about the relationship of the Inuit to the caribou:
—What is wished for the caribou?
—What is wished for the hunter?
—Why might the caribou hunt be so important?

Sadness

Before the Selection

136 / TEACHING PLANS SIX AND SEVEN

Tempus Fugit

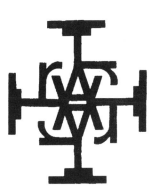

You work for Gaiety Print Novelties, which is going to market a new pocket calendar. By mid-1993, it's almost ready to print. Your supervisor asks you to look through the final (vandyke) proofs. "I don't know where the previous proofs are," he says, handing you a file folder, "but here are the lists of special days that are supposed to be indicated."

The April list looks like this:

```
Moon phases                    3 April
     3rd quarter              11 April
     new                      19 April
     1st quarter              25 April
     full
Holidays                       1 April
     Good Friday               3 April
     Easter                    3 April
     End of Passover           4 April
     Easter Monday             7 April
     World Health Day         22 April
     Earth Day                23 April
     St George's Day
```

April 1994

Sun	Mon	Tues	Wed	Thur	Fri	Sat
					1 Good Friday	2
3 Easter End of Passover	4 Easter Monday	5	6	7 World Health Day	8	9
10	11 ●	12	13	14	15	16
17	18	19 ◑	20	21	22 Earth Day	23 St. George's Day
24 / 31	25 ○	26	27	28	29	30